LEAVING FOOTPRINTS

COVER
ILLUSTRATOR

SPOTLIGHT

GREGORY ALEXANDER

✦ Gregory Alexander lives in Kent, England. He says he decided to become an artist when he was fourteen years old. Today, he likes to travel and then "tell stories in paint" about what he sees. Mr. Alexander has won several important awards for his art and was elected to the Royal Watercolor Society in 1987.

✦ Gregory Alexander's cover painting of a tropical rain forest was inspired by both *The Great Kapok Tree,* a story in this book, and by its title, *Leaving Footprints.*

Acknowledgments appear on page 175, which constitutes an extension of this copyright page.

© 1993 Silver Burdett Ginn Inc.
Cover art © 1993 by Gregory Alexander, R. W. S.

ISBN 0–663–54656–7

4 5 6 7 8 9 10 RRD 98 97 96 95 94

New Dimensions
IN THE
WORLD OF READING

LEAVING
FOOTPRINTS

P R O G R A M   A U T H O R S

James F. Baumann   Roselmina Indrisano   P. David Pearson
Theodore Clymer   Dale D. Johnson   Taffy E. Raphael
Carl Grant   Connie Juel   Marian Davies Toth
Elfrieda H. Hiebert   Jeanne R. Paratore   Richard L. Venezky

SILVER BURDETT GINN

NEEDHAM, MA   MORRISTOWN, NJ
ATLANTA, GA   DALLAS, TX   DEERFIELD, IL   MENLO PARK, CA

Unit 1 Theme

ON YOUR OWN

Unit 2 Theme
Get the Message

ON YOUR OWN

*I*t can be fun to do
things on your own.

What makes some
people so good at
being on their own?

BOY JUGGLING SHELLS, *ink and color on paper by Katsushika Hokusai, Japanese, (1760–1849),
14.76.59.4, © The Metropolitan Museum of Art, New York, Charles Stewart Smith Collection, Gift of Mrs.
Charles Stewart Smith, Charles Stewart Smith, Jr., and Howard Caswell Smith, in Memory of Charles
Stewart Smith, 1914, Photograph by Malcolm Varon*

Theme Books for
On Your Own

Discover how some people find the courage to reach for their dreams—all on their own.

✼ Do you ever wish that you could outwit someone who thinks that he is smarter than you? In *Flossie & the Fox* by Patricia McKissack, a fox thinks he's smart enough to fool clever Flossie.

※ Can you imagine building and flying your own airplanes? That's what Louis Blériot does in *The Glorious Flight* by Alice and Martin Provensen. Even when his planes crash, Louis doesn't stop trying!

More Books to Enjoy

Harriet Tubman by Polly Carter
Roland the Minstrel Pig by William Steig
The Courage of Sarah Noble by Alice Dalgliesh
Chin Chiang and the Dragon's Dance by Ian Wallace

THE RECITAL

by Johanna Hurwitz

Anyone who saw Sonia and Maria Torres together knew they were sisters. Both girls had long, dark hair and the same bright, brown eyes. When they smiled, they both had dimples in their cheeks.

Although the sisters looked alike, they were very different. Maria took piano lessons and loved making music. Sonia loved music, too, but she loved sports even more. Sonia was one of the best players on the girls' soccer team at school.

One hot afternoon after soccer practice, Sonia carefully opened the front door to her house. She could hear Maria playing music, and she didn't want to bother her. Quietly, Sonia walked into the kitchen and opened the refrigerator to get a glass of orange juice.

"Get a glass of juice for me, too," said Maria as she came into the kitchen.

"Did I make too much noise?" asked Sonia. "Sorry."

"You weren't noisy," said Maria. "I've been practicing all afternoon for Mrs. Howard's recital, and I was getting ready to take a break."

Sonia nodded her head. It was a real honor to be asked to play in Mrs. Howard's recital, and Maria had been taking lessons for only two years. Most of the students who would be playing had been studying with Mrs. Howard for four or five years.

"I bet you're one of Mrs. Howard's best students," said Sonia.

"I know I play well when I'm at home," Maria said, "but I'm scared to go on stage. What if I make some awful mistakes?"

Sonia gave Maria a hug. "Don't be afraid," she said. "Just relax and pretend you're playing at home and that no one is listening but me."

"I'll try," Maria said.

Two weeks later the recital took place. That morning when she awoke, Maria said that her stomach hurt.

"You're probably just nervous," said Mrs. Torres.

"You should go running with me," said Sonia.

"Running?" said Maria. "You're the runner, not me."

"I know," laughed Sonia. "But if you run with me, it'll help you relax."

"It can't hurt," said Mrs. Torres.

The two sisters ran around the block three times. Sonia ran slowly so that her sister could keep up with her.

"Don't you feel better already?" Sonia asked. "Coach Reynolds says that lively movement, such as running, clears the head."

"What does she say about making mistakes at a recital?" asked Maria.

"She says that if you make a mistake, you just concentrate harder and keep on going. Don't forget the terrible mistake I made in the first game my team played this year," Sonia said.

"What was that?" asked Maria. "I don't remember."

"I kicked the ball in the wrong direction and made a goal for the other team. I was so embarrassed. Imagine helping the other team score! It was awful."

"What did your coach say?" asked Maria.

"She said to concentrate on the next goal and not to look back on the past," Sonia answered. "You know, she was right. I concentrated on the game, and I didn't think about what had already happened. Before long, I scored a goal for our team."

The girls ran back to the house. Maria was out of breath from her run, but her stomach no longer hurt. They showered and dressed for the recital.

At the front of the recital hall there was a sign showing the way to the room for Mrs. Howard's recital. The room was large, and there seemed to be over a hundred chairs lined up for the audience.

Maria was beginning to look pale and frightened. Sonia squeezed her sister's hand.

"Good luck," Sonia whispered to Maria.

Mrs. Howard got up in front of the audience and announced the name of the first student. He looked old enough to be in high school. Sonia watched as he walked stiffly toward the piano. He had black hair, and his face had turned bright red. He looked nervous, too.

The piece that the young man played was one that Sonia had heard Maria practicing at home a long time ago. He played it faster than Maria did. When he was finished, everyone clapped politely.

The next student was a grown woman. She played her piece very slowly, as if she were being extra careful not to make any mistakes. Again, the audience clapped when she finished playing.

Sonia took a deep breath. She listened as Mrs. Howard announced Maria's name and watched her sister as she slowly made her way towards the piano.

Maria sat down on the piano bench with her hands in her lap. Everyone waited for her to begin.

Maria played the opening notes of her piece, but then she made a mistake and stopped. For a moment it looked as if she were going to run off the stage. Sonia held her breath as she looked at her sister. Maria was sitting very stiffly. "You can do it. You can do it," Sonia whispered to herself, wishing that Maria could hear her. She knew how Maria was feeling. Then Maria took a deep breath. She bent toward the keyboard and started again from the beginning of her piece.

Sonia sat back in her chair to listen. The air was filled with the most wonderful sounds. If Maria was still nervous, you could not hear it in her music.

When the music ended, the audience clapped loudly. Everyone could tell that Maria had real talent. The other students had played the notes, but Maria had played music.

After the recital was over, Mrs. Howard shook hands with Mr. and Mrs. Torres. "Maria is my prize student," she said, hugging Maria. "I know you are proud of her."

Maria stood next to Sonia. "I couldn't have done it without your help," she whispered.

"What did I do?" asked Sonia.

"I was going to run off the stage after I made that first mistake, but then I remembered what you told me about soccer. You said that concentrating was the most important thing, and you said not to look back. So I started over, and if I made a little mistake, I just kept on going. I didn't let it upset me."

Sonia was amazed. "I can't believe that tips for playing soccer would be useful for playing the piano!" she laughed.

"Do you have any piano tips to help me play soccer?" Sonia asked Maria. It was something to look into.

Reader's Response ～ Have you ever felt the way Maria did before the recital? If so, how did you deal with it?

Library Link ～ *If you enjoyed this story by Johanna Hurwitz, you might enjoy reading her other books, such as* Aldo Applesauce, Aldo Ice Cream, Class Clown, *and* Yellow Blue Jay.

DID YOU KNOW...

It sometimes takes a whole year to build a piano. As many as four hundred people may work on the piano during that time.

The wood used to make the piano is dried in an oven— sometimes for as long as three months— to remove moisture.

The largest piano is called a concert grand piano. It weighs about 1,000 pounds and may have as many as 12,000 parts.

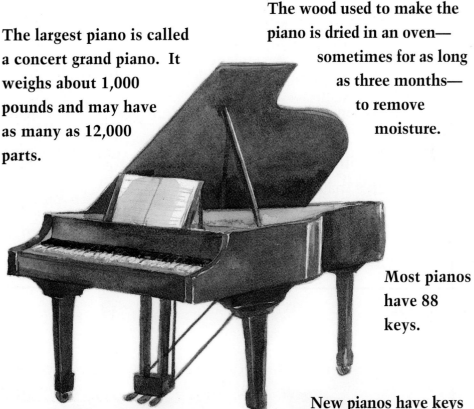

Most pianos have 88 keys.

Piano keys used to be coated with ivory from elephant tusks. Today, in many countries it's against the law to kill elephants for their tusks.

New pianos have keys made of wood coated with plastic. This works better because plastic doesn't yellow with age the way ivory does.

What piano facts can you think of?

Johanna Hurwitz

Johanna Hurwitz always knew she would be a writer.

"When I was about eight or nine years old, I made up stories to tell to my younger brother," she says. "I started writing them down. I even sent some to children's magazines."

At the age of ten, she wrote and published her first poem, titled ''Books.'' It was about what books meant to her. Mrs. Hurwitz was paid fifty cents for the poem. The fifty cents was sent to her by check!

Mrs. Hurwitz was born and raised in the Bronx, in New York City. ''My home was filled with books,'' she says. ''Some of my happiest early memories were when my father and mother read to me. I lived in a neighborhood that was filled with children. I could walk to the library, and I did so almost every day. The library was my other home. I loved it so much that I decided by the age of ten that someday I would become a librarian. I also knew then that I would one day write books.''

In high school, Mrs. Hurwitz started working in a public library. After graduating from college, she became a full-time children's librarian.

She still finds time from her busy writing schedule to work part-time as a children's librarian at the Great Neck Library in Great Neck, New York. There she reads to children and tells them stories. ''I'll never stop working in libraries,'' she says. ''I love it so much.''

Mrs. Hurwitz and her husband, Uri, a teacher and writer, have two grown children, Nomi and Beni. She made up stories to tell to her children when they were young. It was not until they were in school that she began to write the stories down.

Her first book, *Busybody Nora*, a story about a six-year-old girl who lives in an apartment in New York City, was published in 1976. Since then she has written almost twenty books.

"My ideas come from everywhere—from my own children, and from children I meet and work with when I visit schools and libraries," she says. "Sometimes, something that someone says, or something that I see on the street or on television will give me an idea.

"When I am not writing, I like to cook and listen to music. Both food and music have crept into several of my books. In *Busybody Nora*, the folk tales *Jack and the Beanstalk* and *Stone Soup* play an important part in the book." Food has also crept into some of the titles of her books, such as *Aldo Ice Cream* and *Aldo Applesauce*.

Another favorite hobby she enjoys is baseball. "I'm a baseball fanatic," she says. Her book *Baseball Fever* came about because of her love of the sport. "I grew up near New York's Yankee Stadium," she says. "I could hear the fans' screaming and cheering coming from the stadium every time a player hit a home run. Loving baseball as I do, it was natural for me to write *Baseball Fever*. I've got it!"

I asked Mrs. Hurwitz if she had any advice to give to young writers. "Yes," she said. "I would like boys and girls to know that writing does not come easily. If you want to be a good baseball player or a fine ballet dancer, you must practice, practice, practice. To become a fine writer, you must practice, also.

"Reading is very important, too. If you want to become a writer, read a lot. The more you read, the larger your vocabulary becomes. Also, the more you read, the more you become aware of how a story really works."

The story you have just read, "The Recital," was written by Mrs. Hurwitz especially for this book.

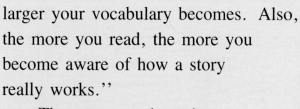

"Like most stories," she says, "it was made up. When I was a young girl, though, I did take piano lessons, and I did not like playing in front of people."

In "The Recital," Maria's sister tells her to concentrate on the next goal and not to look back at mistakes. "Writers should also remember not to look back at mistakes," she says. "If baseball players make mistakes in games and keep thinking about the mistakes, the rest of the game will not go as well for them. You should just think about the next thing you are going to do—as Maria did. You really have to forget past mistakes and keep going.

"Whatever you do in life, believe in yourself. Don't give up. Keep plugging away. Whether you are running in a marathon race, or creating a piece of artwork, or writing a poem, story, or a report, stay with it. Believe in it."

Reader's Response ∾ How do you feel about Johanna Hurwitz's advice, "Believe in yourself. Don't give up"?

Getting Started

Like Johanna Hurwitz, the American poet Langston Hughes began writing when he was still in school. It all began when he was elected class poet:

"The day I was elected, I went home and wondered what I should write. Since we had eight teachers in our school, I thought there should be one verse for each teacher, with an especially good one for my favorite teacher, Miss Ethel Welsh. And since the teachers were to have eight verses, I felt the class should have eight, too. So my first poem was about the longest poem I ever wrote—sixteen verses, which were later cut down. In the first half of the poem, I said that our school had the finest teachers there ever were. And in the latter half, I said our class was the greatest class ever graduated. So at graduation, when I read the poem, naturally everybody applauded loudly."

"That was the way I began to write poetry."

Jason Wants a Library

by
Margaret Tuley Patton

Every time ten-year-old Jason Hardman wanted a book from a library, he borrowed his sister's bike and pedaled six miles to the next town, Monroe. Since Jason's favorite thing to do was to read books, he spent hours pedaling.

Jason's town of Elsinore, Utah, had only 650 people, too tiny for a library of its own. Elsinore was so small that the children even went to school in Monroe.

One night, Jason said to his parents, "I want to start a library in Elsinore." They were pleased but told him that he would have to talk with the town council.

This is Jason, the boy who wants a library.

"What is a town council?" Jason asked.

"It's a group of about eight elected members and the mayor. They run all the town's business," his mom said. "Elsinore, like all towns, collects taxes from its citizens and uses the money for public services, such as fire and police protection," she explained.

"But the town can't afford a library," his dad added.

"Maybe I can run it for the town," Jason said.

Talking to nine adults sounded scary, but Jason wanted to give it a try.

On the night of the next council meeting, he and his father went to the town hall. A two-storied stone building constructed in the 1890s, White Rock School was now the town hall. There in a large room he found the council members sitting around an oval table talking about town matters. They barely looked up when Jason came into the room. The council was talking about the new fire engine and how to fix the roads. The mayor, a thin, serious-looking man, sometimes looked over in Jason's direction. A council member, a gray-haired woman with large gold earrings, also watched him.

When it was Jason's time, *everyone* looked at him. At first he hesitated, then began to speak. "I want to start a library in Elsinore. It needs one very badly."

The council listened closely. Jason spent almost an hour talking with the council.

"We'll have to think about it," the mayor finally said to the brown-haired boy.

"At least they didn't say no," Jason told his parents after the meeting.

A week went by without any news from the town hall. Jason phoned the mayor at his home to ask if a decision had been made about the library. The mayor answered, "The council is still thinking about it."

Another week passed. Every day when Jason came off the school bus, he'd ask his mother: "Did the mayor phone?" Each day, the answer was, "No." Jason phoned the mayor every night for two weeks. Each night, the same answer was given: "The council is still thinking about it." Jason grew tired of waiting. "Why can't I use the town hall basement for my library?" he thought to himself.

During those weeks, Jason pedaled often to Monroe for library books. "I wonder if I will be biking these six miles forever for a book?" he asked himself sadly. He began to doubt that he would ever get a library for Elsinore.

At last it happened. When he phoned the mayor, Jason was invited to the council's next meeting. The mayor told him they might find space in the town hall basement. It was just too good to be true.

When Jason wanted library books, he pedaled six miles.

When Jason entered the council room and saw them all sitting at the oval table, he suddenly felt terrible. He just knew that they had changed their minds. The mayor, with a stern face, turned toward Jason and asked him to come to the oval table. Jason sat down in the straight-back chair.

The council began asking him questions. Someone asked how many days the library would be open. "Tuesdays and Thursdays from 4 to 6 P.M.," Jason answered quietly.

At last, the mayor looked across the table and said in a firm voice, "After weeks of thinking, we have decided that you can use a room in the basement for a public library."

Jason was so shocked he could hardly speak. Now all the council members and the mayor smiled and wished him good luck. "We figure that you can run a library the right way, and we want to give you the chance," the mayor said. Jason almost danced out of the meeting.

In the next few weeks, Jason told every person he knew in Elsinore that he was opening a library in the town hall. He went to the Elsinore Literary Club asking for books. Then he began to phone people he didn't know throughout Sevier County. The *Richfield Reaper,* a weekly newspaper from the town of Richfield, wrote about Jason's plans for a library. Soon, the two daily papers in Salt Lake City wrote stories about Jason wanting books. One of the headlines read,

Young Librarian Opens Library—Needs Books!

Jason had to work hard to get his library books organized.

People mailed boxes of books to Jason's home. "Awesome! Where am I going to fit all these books?" Jason said, grinning. He knew that before long he would have enough books to open his library.

Jason, his older sister and brother, and his parents spent two months cleaning out the town hall basement and putting books on shelves. Jason arranged the books in a system so people could find what they wanted easily. His friends and their parents also came to help.

Jason's mother and friends helped, too.

The library opened on Election Day, November 4, 1980. Almost one hundred people came to see the new library. Jason was so tickled. His best friend Dennis Jensen helped Jason in the library after school. In the first year, Elsinore library had about one thousand books. It was a very busy place.

Soon worldwide newspapers wrote articles about Jason's new library. Jason appeared on various television shows, including *Good Morning America, Fantasy, The Phil Donahue Show,* and even *The Tonight Show.* On *The Tonight Show,* Johnny Carson asked Jason if there was anything his parents didn't want him to say on television. Jason hesitated, then responded, ''They told me not to ask for any more books.'' More bags full of books flooded Elsinore after the show.

At age eleven, Jason spoke at a joint congressional hearing in Washington, D.C., about the needs of rural America. "Why should I suffer because I live in Elsinore without a library? Salt Lake City has plenty of libraries. Why should my friends suffer?" he asked the joint panel.

Jason went to the White House two times to talk to President Ronald Reagan. *Reading Rainbow* filmed Jason in his library to encourage children to read books in the summer months. *Reader's Digest* wrote a story about Jason.

Jason meets President Ronald Reagan.

Here, Jason sits in his library enjoying a good book.

Jason is a bit embarrassed about all the fuss made over him. He just did what he thought was needed in Elsinore. By the time he was eighteen years old, his library had sixteen thousand books and occupied two rooms in the town hall basement.

Jason and the council have discussed the future of the library. It will continue to stay open for others who want a library in Elsinore.

Reader's Response ～ What would you like to do to help *your* community?

Library Link ～ *If you enjoyed this selection and would like to read something else about young people doing things on their own, read* Summer Business *by Charles Martin.*

Kids *Did* It!

Nine-year-old Roland Tiensuu had a great idea—an idea that would grow in the hearts of children all over the world.

This is how it happened. In 1987, a biologist came to Roland's classroom in Sweden. She explained what is happening to our rain forests and the plants and animals that live in them. Then Roland got his big idea. Why not raise money to buy some land in a rain forest? he asked. Roland's idea led to the establishment of an international children's rain forest, the Bosque Eterno de los Niños.

Roland and his classmates made and sold paintings and picture books and gave a performance about the rain forest. They earned enough money to buy fifteen acres of rain forest in Monteverde, Costa Rica, which is in Central America. Other children learned about what Roland and his friends were doing and joined in. In all, children have raised more than one million dollars and Bosque Eterno de los Niños has grown to over 18,000 acres.

This visitor to the Bosque Eterno de los Niños meets a giant salamander.

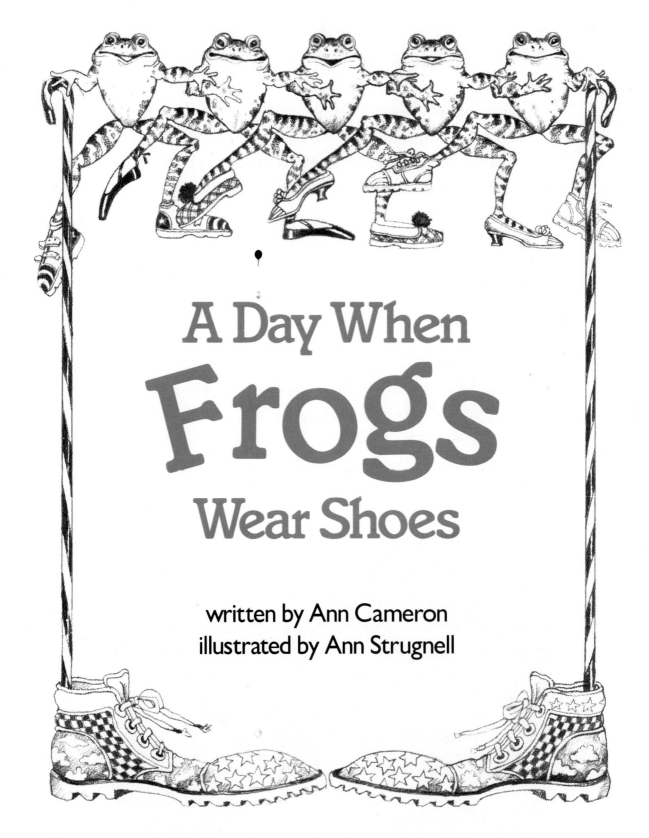

A Day When Frogs Wear Shoes

written by Ann Cameron
illustrated by Ann Strugnell

My little brother, Huey, my best friend, Gloria, and I were sitting on our front steps. It was one of those hot summer days when everything stands still. We didn't know what to do. We were watching the grass grow. It didn't grow fast.

"You know something?" Gloria said. "This is a slow day."

"It's so slow the dogs don't bark," Huey said.

"It's so slow the flies don't fly," Gloria said.

"It's so slow ice cream wouldn't melt," I said.

"If we had any ice cream," Huey said.

"But we don't," Gloria said.

We watched the grass some more.

"We better do something," I said.

"Like what?" Gloria asked.

"We could go visit Dad," Huey said.

"That's a *terrible* idea," I said.

"Why?" Huey asked. "I like visiting Dad."

My father has a shop about a mile from our house, where he fixes cars. Usually it is fun to visit him. If he has customers, he always introduces us as if we were important guests. If he doesn't have company, sometimes he lets us ride in the cars he puts up on the lift. Sometimes he buys us treats.

"Huey," I said, "usually, visiting Dad is a good idea. Today, it's a dangerous idea."

"Why?" Gloria said.

"Because we're bored," I said. "My dad hates it when people are bored. He says the world is so interesting nobody should ever be bored."

"I see," Gloria said, as if she didn't.

"So we'll go see him," Huey said, "and we just won't tell him we're bored. We're bored, but we won't tell him."

"Just so you remember that!" I said.

"Oh, I'll remember," Huey said.

Huey was wearing his angel look. When he has that look, you know he'll never remember anything.

Huey and I put on sweat bands. Gloria put on dark glasses. We started out.

The sun shined up at us from the sidewalks. Even the shadows on the street were hot as blankets.

Huey picked up a stick and scratched it along the sidewalk. "Oh, we're bored," he muttered. "Bored, bored, bored, bored, bored!"

"Huey!" I yelled. I wasn't bored anymore. I was nervous.

Finally we reached a sign:

RALPH'S CAR HOSPITAL
Punctures
Rust
Dents & Bashes
Bad Brakes
Bad Breaks
Unusual Complaints

That's my dad's sign. My dad is Ralph.

The parking lot had three cars in it. Dad was inside the shop, lifting the hood of another car. He didn't have any customers with him, so we didn't get to shake hands and feel like visiting mayors or congressmen.

"Hi, Dad," I said.

"Hi!" my dad said.

"We're—" Huey said.

I didn't trust Huey. I stepped on his foot.

"We're on a hike," I said.

"Well, nice of you to stop by," my father said. "If you want, you can stay awhile and help me."

"O.K.," we said.

So Huey sorted nuts and bolts. Gloria shined fenders with a rag. I held a new windshield wiper while my dad put it on a car window.

"Nice work, Huey and Julian and Gloria!" my dad said when we were done.

And then he sent us to the store across the street to buy paper cups and ice cubes and a can of frozen lemonade.

We mixed the lemonade in the shop. Then we sat out under the one tree by the side of the driveway and drank all of it.

"Good lemonade!" my father said. "So what are you kids going to do now?"

"Oh, hike!" I said.

"You know," my father answered, "I'm surprised at you kids picking a hot day like today for a hike. The ground is so hot. On a day like this, frogs wear shoes!"

"They do?" Huey said.

"Especially if they go hiking," my father said. "Of course, a lot of frogs, on a day like this, would stay home. So I wonder why you kids are hiking."

Sometimes my father notices too much. Then he gets yellow lights shining in his eyes, asking you to tell the whole truth. That's when I know to look at my feet.

"Oh," I said, "we *like* hiking."

But Gloria didn't know any better. She looked into my father's eyes. "Really," she said, "this wasn't a real hike. We came to see you."

"Oh, I see!" my father said, looking pleased.

"Because we were bored," Huey said.

My father jumped up so fast he tipped over his lemonade cup. "BORED!" my father yelled. "You were BORED?"

He picked up his cup and waved it in the air.

"And you think *I* don't get BORED?" my father roared, sprinkling out a few last drops of lemonade from his cup. "You think I don't get bored fixing cars when it's hot enough that frogs wear shoes?"

"'This is such an interesting world that nobody should ever be bored.' That's what you said," I reminded him.

"Last week," Huey added.

"Ummm," my father said. He got quiet.

He rubbed his hand over his mouth, the way he does when he's thinking.

"Why, of course," my father said, "I remember that. And it's the perfect, absolute truth. People absolutely SHOULD NOT get bored! However—" He paused. "It just happens that, sometimes, they do."

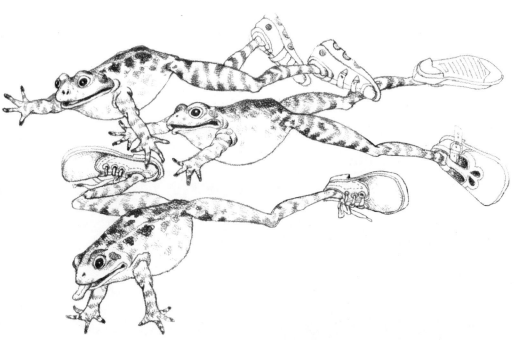

My father rubbed a line in the dirt with his shoe. He was thinking so hard I could see his thoughts standing by the tree and sitting on all the fenders of the cars.

"You know, if you three would kindly help me some more, I could leave a half hour early, and we could drive down by the river."

"We'll help," I said.

"Yes, and then we can look for frogs!" Huey said. So we stayed. We learned how to make a signal light blink. And afterward, on the way to the river, my dad bought us all ice cream cones. The ice cream did melt. Huey's melted all down the front of his shirt. It took him ten paper napkins and the river to clean up.

After Huey's shirt was clean, we took our shoes and socks off and went wading.

We looked for special rocks under the water—the ones that are beautiful until you take them out of the water, when they get dry and not so bright.

We found skipping stones and tried to see who could get the most skips from a stone.

We saw a school of minnows going as fast as they could to get away from us.

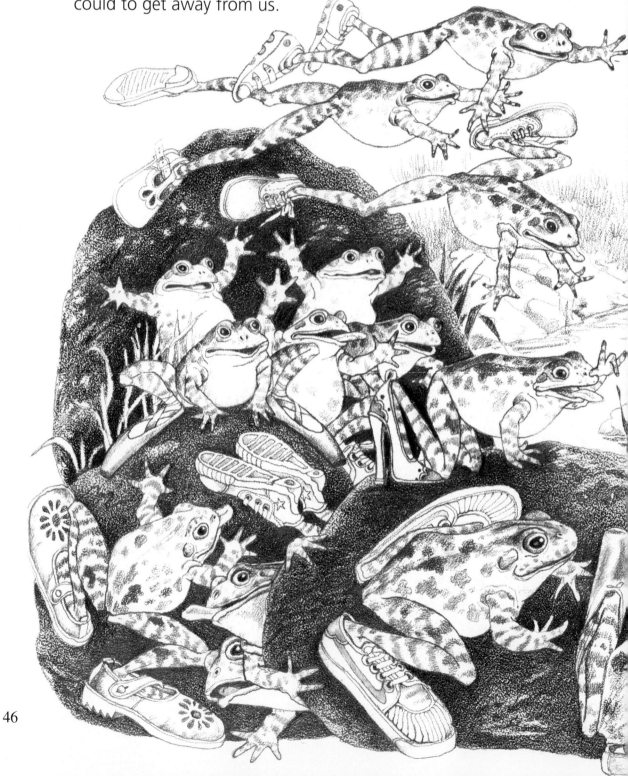

But we didn't see any frogs.

"If you want to see frogs," my father said, "you'll have to walk down the bank a ways and look hard."

So we decided to do that.

"Fine!" my father said. "But I'll stay here. I think I'm ready for a little nap."

"Naps are boring!" we said.

"Sometimes it's nice to be bored," my father said.

We left him with his eyes closed, sitting under a tree.

Huey saw the first frog. He almost stepped on it. It jumped into the water, and we ran after it.

Huey caught it and picked it up, and then I saw another one. I grabbed it.

It was slippery and strong and its body was cold, just like it wasn't the middle of summer.

Then Gloria caught one too. The frogs wriggled in our hands, and we felt their hearts beating. Huey looked at their funny webbed feet.

"Their feet are good for swimming," he said, "but Dad is wrong. They don't wear shoes!"

"No way," Gloria said. "They sure don't wear shoes."

"Let's go tell him," I said.

We threw our frogs back into the river. They made little trails swimming away from us. And then we went back to my father.

He was sitting under the tree with his eyes shut. It looked like he hadn't moved an inch.

"We found frogs," Huey said, "and we've got news for you. They don't wear shoes!"

My father's eyes opened. "They don't?" he said. "Well, I can't be right about everything. Dry your feet. Put your shoes on. It's time to go."

We all sat down to put on our shoes.

I pulled out a sock and put it on.

I stuck my foot into my shoe. My foot wouldn't go in.

I picked up the shoe and looked inside.

"Oh no!" I yelled.

There were two little eyes inside my shoe, looking out at me. Huey and Gloria grabbed their socks. All our shoes had frogs in them, every one.

"What did I tell you," my father said.

"You were right," we said. "It's a day when frogs wear shoes!"

Reader's Response ～ Julian's father said that nobody should ever be bored. What do you think?

Library Link ～ *This story is from the book* More Stories Julian Tells *by Ann Cameron. You might enjoy reading the entire book to find out more about Julian, Gloria, and Huey.*

It's Raining...
Worms and Frogs?

When people say it's raining cats and dogs, they mean it's really raining hard.

Although no one has seen cats and dogs falling from the sky, some people think it rains worms! Why? When it rains hard, water fills the worm holes in the ground, the worms crawl out to keep from drowning and then head for a safe place, like a sidewalk.

Has it ever rained frogs? Early weather records report that, once during a hailstorm, frogs really did fall from the sky. Here's how it may have happened. Air currents picked up tiny frogs and lifted them up into the storm clouds. Then water droplets froze around the frogs, making hail. When the hailstones rained down on people, so did the frogs!

Phillis Wheatley

America's First Black Poet

by Kacey Brown

sad news that Mrs. Wheatley was very ill. Immediately Phillis made plans to return to Boston. She wanted to get back to Boston as soon as she could so that she could be with Mrs. Wheatley. Phillis did get back in time to see Mrs. Wheatley, who died a short time later. Mr. Wheatley died soon after. Even though these events caused great sadness for Phillis, she continued to write. Now she was writing not only for herself but also for the Wheatleys, who had helped her so much.

Phillis Meets George Washington

Not long after Phillis returned to Boston, America began its war ⌐ainst England. Americans ⌐nted to be free from England's To prepare for the war, ⌐al George Washington went bridge, Massachusetts, as the American army. It ⌐xciting time for people ⌐ton area! They were ⌐et the man who ⌐hem in their struggle ⌐hillis had heard ⌐ashington. She ⌐ a great man.

National Portrait Gallery, Smithsonian Institution

A few months later, she wrote a letter to General Washington to wish him success. In her letter, she included a poem she had written about him. Part of the poem read:

Thee, first in peace and honours . . .
Fam'd for thy valour, for thy virtues
more. . . .

General Washington was so pleased with the poem that he sent Phillis a personal thank-you note and invited her to visit him in Cambridge, Massachusetts. Phillis was delighted.

Phillis Wheatley, the shy young girl who came to Boston as a slave in 1761, met and talked to the man who would become the first president of the United States. She had come to Boston unable to read or write and later went on to become a well-known poet. Phillis Wheatley's poetry is an example of what a young person can accomplish on her own.

Reader's Response ∽ If you could ask Phillis Wheatley one question, what would it be?

Signing the Declaration of Independence

Can you imagine working on one painting for more than ten years? John Trumbull did it! He began this painting in 1786 and finished it eleven years later. Why did it take him so long?

Trumbull decided to paint the men who signed this historic document in person. He felt he could make them look more lifelike that way. He traveled all over the world looking for these men. As he found each one, he usually sketched or painted him in miniature. Sometimes he painted him directly into the picture. Trumbull found thirty-six. Others were painted from pictures or memory.

Why do you think he went to so much trouble?

59

John Trumbull, *The Declaration of Independence, 4 July 1776*, copyright Yale University Art Gallery

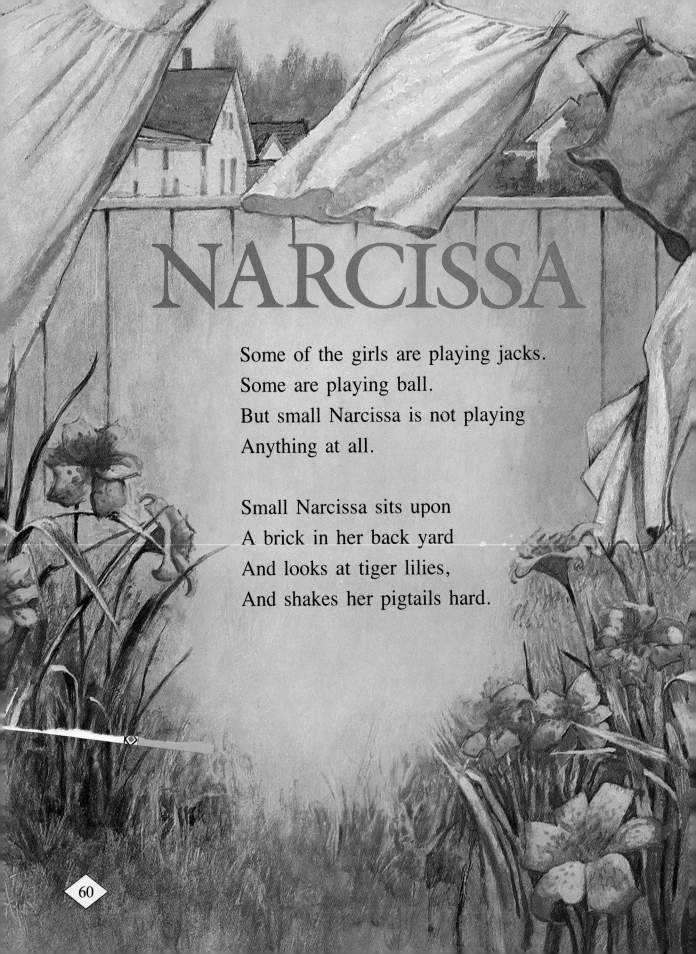

NARCISSA

Some of the girls are playing jacks.
Some are playing ball.
But small Narcissa is not playing
Anything at all.

Small Narcissa sits upon
A brick in her back yard
And looks at tiger lilies,
And shakes her pigtails hard.

First she is an ancient queen
In pomp and purple veil.
Soon she is a singing wind.
And, next, a nightingale.

How fine to be Narcissa,
A-changing like all that!
While sitting still, as still, as still
As anyone ever sat!

Gwendolyn Brooks

61

Alexander
Horrible, No Good,

and the Terrible, Very Bad Day

written by Judith Viorst
illustrated by Ray Cruz

I went to sleep with gum in my mouth and now there's gum in my hair and when I got out of bed this morning I tripped on the skateboard and by mistake I dropped my sweater in the sink while the water was running and I could tell it was going to be a terrible, horrible, no good, very bad day.

At breakfast Anthony found a Corvette Sting Ray car kit in his breakfast cereal box and Nick found a Junior Undercover Agent code ring in his breakfast cereal box but in my breakfast cereal box all I found was breakfast cereal.

I think I'll move to Australia.

In the car pool Mrs. Gibson let Becky have a seat by the window. Audrey and Elliott got seats by the window too. I said I was being scrunched. I said I was being smushed. I said, if I don't get a seat by the window I am going to be carsick. No one even answered.

I could tell it was going to be a terrible, horrible, no good, very bad day.

At school Mrs. Dickens liked Paul's picture of the sailboat better than my picture of the invisible castle.

At singing time she said I sang too loud. At counting time she said I left out sixteen. Who needs sixteen?

I could tell it was going to be a terrible, horrible, no good, very bad day.

I could tell because Paul said I wasn't his best friend anymore. He said that Philip Parker was his best friend and that Albert Moyo was his next best friend and that I was only his third best friend.

I hope you sit on a tack, I said to Paul. I hope the next time you get a double-decker strawberry ice-cream cone the ice cream part falls off the cone part and lands in Australia.

There were two cupcakes in Philip Parker's lunch bag and Albert got a Hershey bar with almonds and Paul's mother gave him a piece of jelly roll that had little coconut sprinkles on the top. Guess whose mother forgot to put in dessert?

It was a terrible, horrible, no good, very bad day.

That's what it was, because after school my mom took us all to the dentist and Dr. Fields found a cavity just in me. Come back next week and I'll fix it, said Dr. Fields.

Next week, I said, I'm going to Australia.

On the way downstairs the elevator door closed on my foot and while we were waiting for my mom to go get the car Anthony made me fall where it was muddy and then when I started crying because of the mud Nick said I was a crybaby and while I was punching Nick for saying crybaby my mom came back with the car and scolded me for being muddy and fighting.

I am having a terrible, horrible, no good, very bad day, I told everybody. No one even answered.

So then we went to the shoestore to buy some sneakers. Anthony chose white ones with blue stripes. Nick chose red ones with white stripes. I chose blue ones with red stripes but then the shoe man said, We're all sold out. They made me buy plain old white ones, but they can't make me wear them.

When we picked up my dad at his office he said I couldn't play with his copying machine, but I forgot. He also said to watch out for the books on his desk, and I was careful as could be except for my elbow. He also said don't fool around with his phone, but I think I called Australia. My dad said please don't pick him up anymore.

It was a terrible, horrible, no good, very bad day.

There were lima beans for dinner and I hate limas.

There was kissing on TV and I hate kissing.

My bath was too hot, I got soap in my eyes, my marble went down the drain, and I had to wear my railroad-train pajamas. I hate my railroad-train pajamas.

When I went to bed Nick took back the pillow he said I could keep and the Mickey Mouse night light burned out and I bit my tongue.

The cat wants to sleep with Anthony, not with me.

It has been a terrible, horrible, no good, very bad day.

My mom says some days are like that.
Even in Australia.

Reader's Response ∿ Why do you think Alexander said he wanted to move to Australia? Have you ever felt the way he did?

Library Link ∿ *If you enjoyed this story by Judith Viorst, you might enjoy reading some poems from her book,* If I Were in Charge of the World and Other Worries.

Get the Message

*Talking, writing
signaling, signing —
why do people send their
messages in different ways?*

THE LETTER, ca. 1891, Mary Stevenson Cassatt, American, 1844–1926. Color print with dry point, soft-ground and aquatint. 13⅝ x 8⅞ in. Gift of William Emerson and Charles Henry Hayden Fund, Courtesy, Museum of Fine Arts, Boston

Theme Books for

Get the Message

*P*eople use smiles, frowns, and actions, as well as words, to tell you what they think or how they feel. Stories often send messages, too. Read and think. It's fun to get the message.

✦ In *The Gold Coin* by Alma Flor Ada, Juan sees Doña Josefa rubbing a gold coin and resolves to get the whole treasure. Will he find the riches he seeks, or something entirely different?

72

Where is the secret to the wise woman's wisdom? In *The Wise Woman and Her Secret* by Eve Merriam, the villagers busily search everywhere for the woman's great secret. How will Jenny ever find it if all she does is daydream?

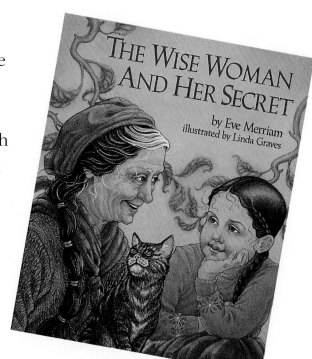

A Drop of Honey by Djemma Bider
Train Whistles by Helen Roney Sattler
The Seeing Stick by Jane Yolen
Finger Rhymes by Marc Brown

THE GREAT KAPOK TREE

In the Amazon rain forest it is always hot, and in that heat everything grows, and grows, and grows. The tops of the trees in the rain forest are called the canopy. The canopy is a sunny place that touches the sky. The animals that live there like lots of light. Colorful parrots fly from tree to tree. Monkeys leap from branch to branch. The bottom of the rain forest is called the understory. The animals that live in the understory like darkness. There, silent snakes curl around hanging vines. Graceful jaguars watch and wait.

And in this steamy environment the great Kapok tree shoots up through the forest and emerges above the canopy.

This is the story of a community of animals that live in one such tree in the rain forest.

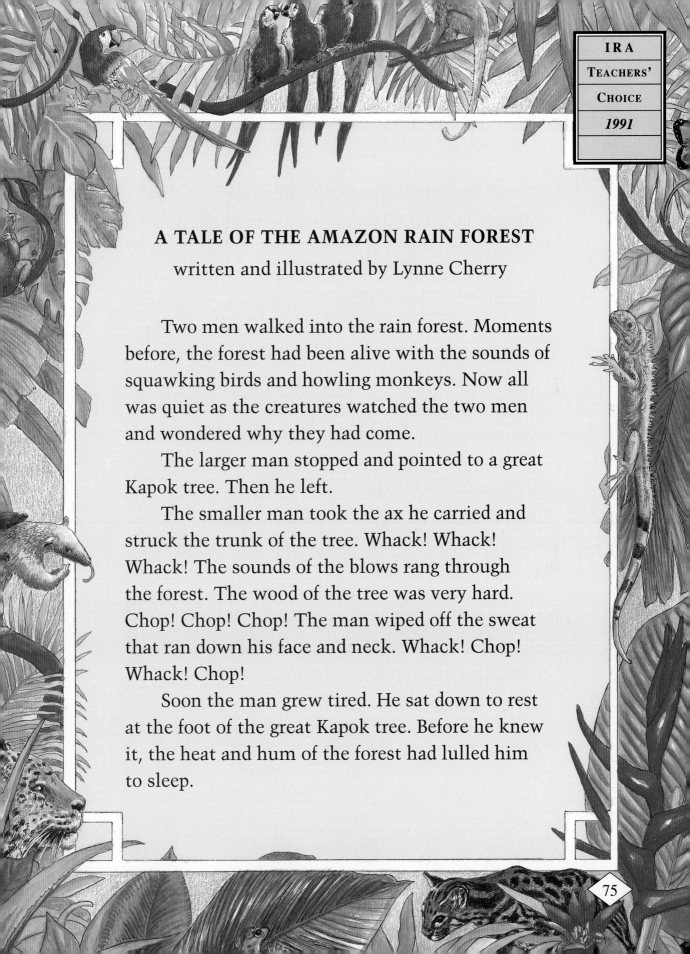

A TALE OF THE AMAZON RAIN FOREST

written and illustrated by Lynne Cherry

Two men walked into the rain forest. Moments before, the forest had been alive with the sounds of squawking birds and howling monkeys. Now all was quiet as the creatures watched the two men and wondered why they had come.

The larger man stopped and pointed to a great Kapok tree. Then he left.

The smaller man took the ax he carried and struck the trunk of the tree. Whack! Whack! Whack! The sounds of the blows rang through the forest. The wood of the tree was very hard. Chop! Chop! Chop! The man wiped off the sweat that ran down his face and neck. Whack! Chop! Whack! Chop!

Soon the man grew tired. He sat down to rest at the foot of the great Kapok tree. Before he knew it, the heat and hum of the forest had lulled him to sleep.

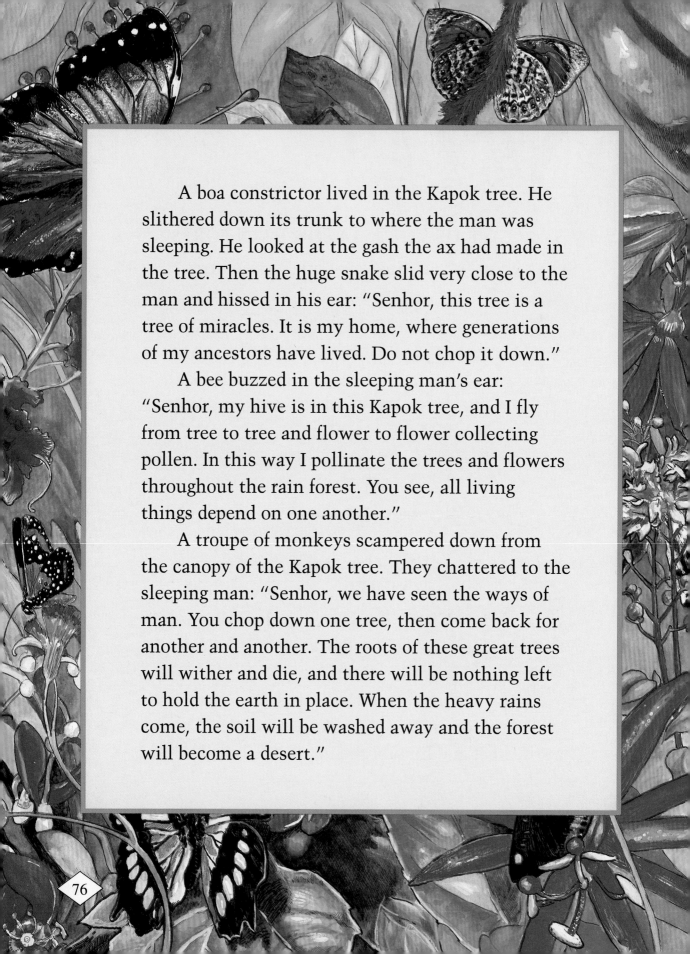

A boa constrictor lived in the Kapok tree. He slithered down its trunk to where the man was sleeping. He looked at the gash the ax had made in the tree. Then the huge snake slid very close to the man and hissed in his ear: "Senhor, this tree is a tree of miracles. It is my home, where generations of my ancestors have lived. Do not chop it down."

A bee buzzed in the sleeping man's ear: "Senhor, my hive is in this Kapok tree, and I fly from tree to tree and flower to flower collecting pollen. In this way I pollinate the trees and flowers throughout the rain forest. You see, all living things depend on one another."

A troupe of monkeys scampered down from the canopy of the Kapok tree. They chattered to the sleeping man: "Senhor, we have seen the ways of man. You chop down one tree, then come back for another and another. The roots of these great trees will wither and die, and there will be nothing left to hold the earth in place. When the heavy rains come, the soil will be washed away and the forest will become a desert."

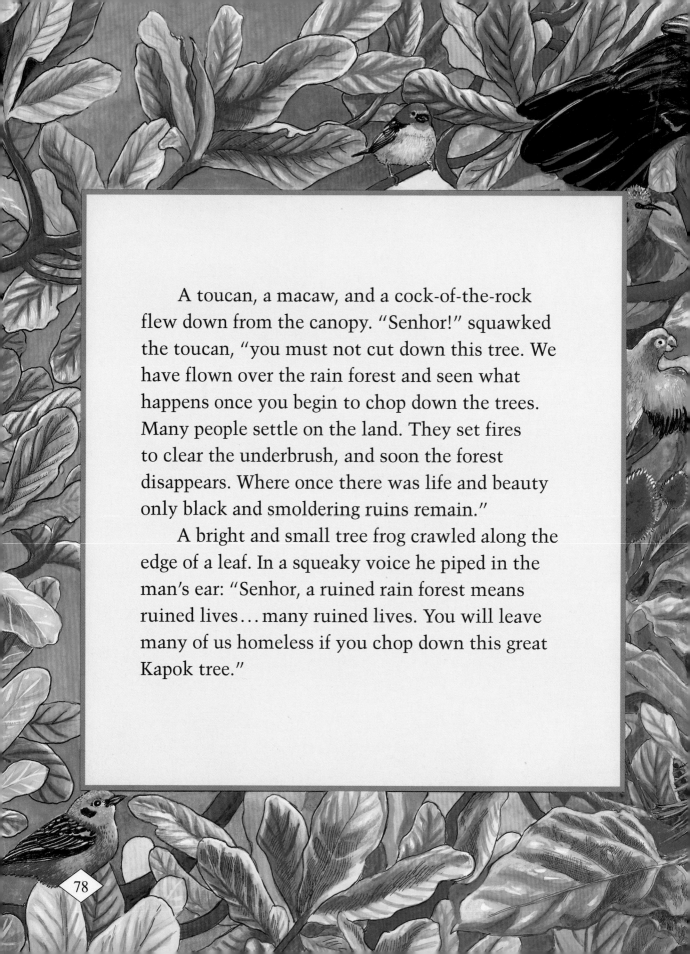

A toucan, a macaw, and a cock-of-the-rock flew down from the canopy. "Senhor!" squawked the toucan, "you must not cut down this tree. We have flown over the rain forest and seen what happens once you begin to chop down the trees. Many people settle on the land. They set fires to clear the underbrush, and soon the forest disappears. Where once there was life and beauty only black and smoldering ruins remain."

A bright and small tree frog crawled along the edge of a leaf. In a squeaky voice he piped in the man's ear: "Senhor, a ruined rain forest means ruined lives... many ruined lives. You will leave many of us homeless if you chop down this great Kapok tree."

A jaguar had been sleeping along a branch in the middle of the tree. Because his spotted coat blended into the dappled light and shadows of the understory, no one had noticed him. Now he leapt down and padded silently over to the sleeping man. He growled in his ear: "Senhor, the Kapok tree is home to many birds and animals. If you cut it down, where will I find my dinner?"

Four tree porcupines swung down from branch to branch and whispered to the man: "Senhor, do you know what we animals and humans need in order to live? Oxygen. And, Senhor, do you know what trees produce? Oxygen! If you cut down the forests you will destroy that which gives us all life."

Several anteaters climbed down the Kapok tree with their young clinging to their backs. The unstriped anteater said to the sleeping man: "Senhor, you are chopping down this tree with no thought for the future. And surely you know that what happens tomorrow depends upon what you do today. The big man tells you to chop down a beautiful tree. He does not think of his own children, who tomorrow must live in a world without trees."

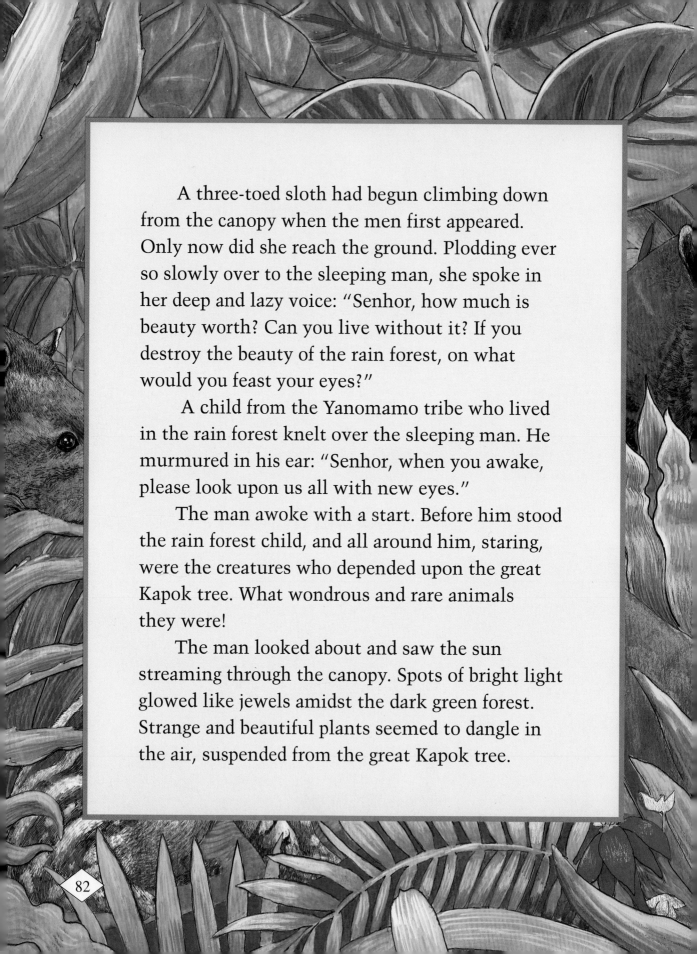

A three-toed sloth had begun climbing down from the canopy when the men first appeared. Only now did she reach the ground. Plodding ever so slowly over to the sleeping man, she spoke in her deep and lazy voice: "Senhor, how much is beauty worth? Can you live without it? If you destroy the beauty of the rain forest, on what would you feast your eyes?"

A child from the Yanomamo tribe who lived in the rain forest knelt over the sleeping man. He murmured in his ear: "Senhor, when you awake, please look upon us all with new eyes."

The man awoke with a start. Before him stood the rain forest child, and all around him, staring, were the creatures who depended upon the great Kapok tree. What wondrous and rare animals they were!

The man looked about and saw the sun streaming through the canopy. Spots of bright light glowed like jewels amidst the dark green forest. Strange and beautiful plants seemed to dangle in the air, suspended from the great Kapok tree.

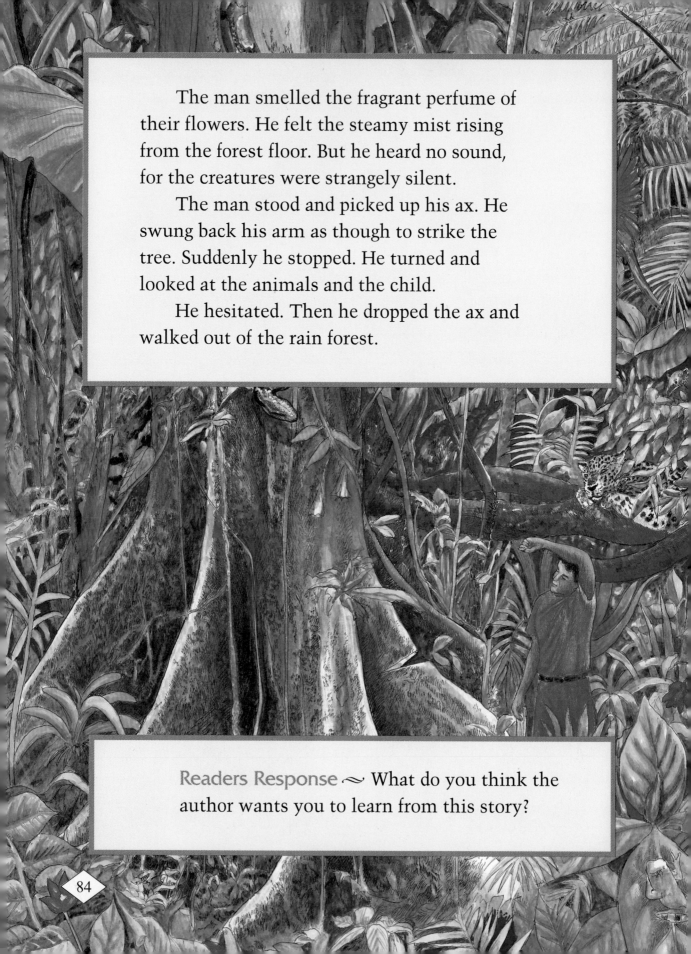

The man smelled the fragrant perfume of their flowers. He felt the steamy mist rising from the forest floor. But he heard no sound, for the creatures were strangely silent.

The man stood and picked up his ax. He swung back his arm as though to strike the tree. Suddenly he stopped. He turned and looked at the animals and the child.

He hesitated. Then he dropped the ax and walked out of the rain forest.

Readers Response ～ What do you think the author wants you to learn from this story?

WHERE IN THE WORLD?

Where in the world would you find a rain forest? The dark green places on the map show where they are. The light green areas show where rain forests have been cut down.

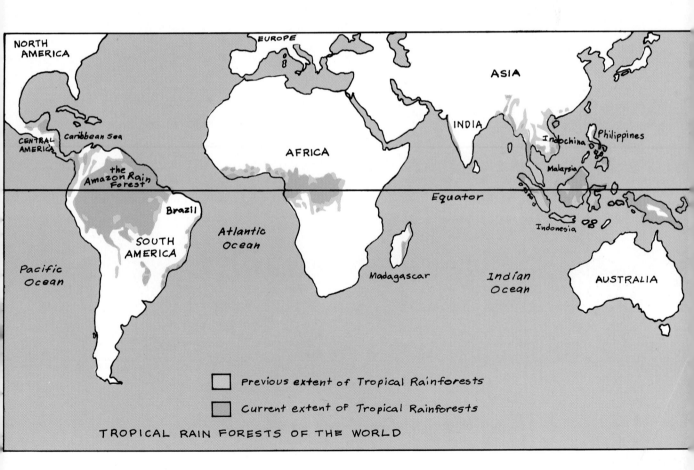

TROPICAL RAIN FORESTS OF THE WORLD

☐ Previous extent of Tropical Rainforests
☐ Current extent of Tropical Rainforests

The Firefly

The rain
Tries without avail
To quench your lamp,
And the rushing wind
But makes it glow
The more.

I believe
That if you flew
Up to the sky
You would twinkle
As a star
Beside the moon.

—Li Po

A giant firefly:
    that way, this way, that way, this—
        and it passes by.

                              —Issa

Words in Our Hands

by Ada B. Litchfield

My name is Michael Turner. I am nine years old. I have two sisters, Gina and Diane, a dog named Polly, and two parents who can't hear me when I talk.

They never have heard me. You see, my mom and dad were born deaf.

Nobody knows for sure why, but it might be because Grandma Ellis had measles before my mother was born and Grandma Turner was in a car accident before my father was born. Sometimes when a mother who is expecting a baby has some disease or is in an accident, the baby is born blind or deaf or is hurt some other way.

My parents never heard any sounds at all when they were babies. Some people think a person who can't hear can't learn to talk. That's not true.

My mom and dad went to a school for deaf kids when they were growing up. That's where they learned to talk. They learned by placing their fingers on their teacher's throat and feeling how words *felt* in her voice box as she said them. They learned how words *looked* by watching her face, especially her lips, as she spoke. It's hard to learn to say words that way. But my parents did.

They don't talk much now, but they can talk. My mother's voice is high and squeaky. My father's is harsh and loud. My parents have never heard other people talking or even their own voices, so they don't know how voices sound. It's not always easy to understand what they are saying, but Gina and Diane and I can.

Sometimes my mother and father can understand what people are saying by reading their lips. That's another thing my parents learned at their school—lip reading.

Reading lips is hard. Some people don't move their lips much when they talk. Or they hide their mouths with their hands or with a moustache. Besides, many words look alike when you say them. Look in the mirror and say *pin* and *bin, hand* and *and, hill* and *ill.* See what I mean?

How we move our bodies and what our faces look like when we talk help our parents read our lips. But most of the time we talk to them with our hands as well as our mouths. Grandma Ellis says we have words in our hands.

One way to talk with your hands is to learn a special alphabet so you can spell words with your fingers. This is called *finger spelling.*

Can you finger spell your name?

The International Manual Alphabet

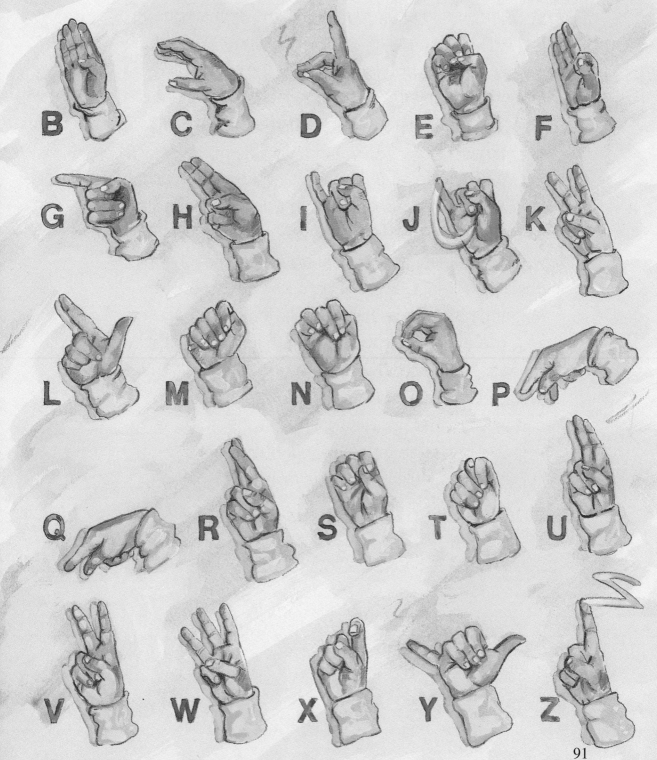

Another way to handtalk is to use sign language. Once you have learned sign language, it is easier and faster than finger spelling.

Oh, sure, everybody uses some sign language. You tell your friends to "go away" without using your voice at all. But sign language for the deaf is like French or Spanish. You have to learn many signs that other people understand before you can talk to anybody.

Gina, Diane, and I are learning new signs all the time. My mother and father learned sign language when they were little. And they taught us signs when we were babies, just as hearing parents teach their children words. Our grandparents, friends, and neighbors helped us learn to talk.

There are five ways Diane can ask my mother for a peanut butter sandwich.

She can make her mouth move slowly so my mother can read her lips.

She can finger spell *peanut butter* like this:

She can ask in sign language. That's easier than finger spelling.

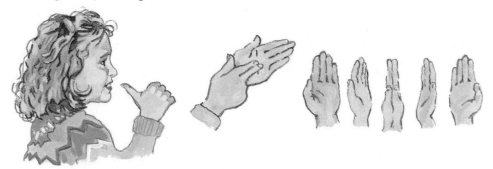

She can print *peanut butter sandwich* on the writing pad my mother always carries with her.

Or she can lead my mother to the jar of peanut butter and point.

My parents have some neat things to help them. In our house, when the telephone or doorbell rings, lights flash on and off. We have a TTY attached to our phone. A TTY is a teletypewriter that spells out messages on tape. Then my parents can type messages back.

Of course, the person calling us has to have a teletypewriter, and not very many people do. That means that many times we kids have to talk on the phone for our parents. And sometimes we have to talk to people who come to the door.

When we were babies, my mother or father checked on us very often to be sure we were all right. They took turns at night. They used a cry alarm, too. A cry alarm is a microphone that is hooked up to a light. When we cried, a light would flash in our parents' bedroom or in the kitchen or living room.

When Diane was little, Gina and I helped take care of her. We would hear when she cried and tell my mom or dad.

Some deaf people have a hearing-ear dog to help them. We have Polly. Polly hasn't had lessons in hand signals the way real hearing-ear dogs have. But she can do many things a hearing-ear dog does.

She gets my mother up by tugging at her blankets if her flashing-light alarm doesn't wake her.

She runs back and forth to let my mom and dad know someone is at the door. She makes a big fuss if a flashing-light alarm goes off or if a pan is boiling over on the stove.

When Diane was a baby, Polly helped take care of her. She still follows Diane around and runs to tell my mother if Diane gets into trouble.

Just because my parents are deaf doesn't mean we don't do things other families do. We go to church. My mom and dad go to programs at school. We go on picnics. We have friends over for dinner and to stay all night. We drive to the city to the Science Museum.

It isn't true that deaf people can't drive a car. Both my parents drive. They just have to depend on their eyes to avoid accidents. That's why my dad put rear view mirrors on both sides of our car.

We are a happy family. At least we were until about six months ago. Then the publishing company where my father has always worked moved to a new town, one hundred miles away.

My father is the editor of a magazine about farming. Nobody in the family wanted to move. But my father loves his job so, of course, he wanted to go with his company.

We bought a new house with a big yard that everybody liked, but it took a long time to get used to our new town. Before, my mom had always done all the shopping and banking for our family. Now she felt a little strange going into a store or bank where the clerks didn't know her. Very often she wanted Gina or me to go with her.

In our old town, everybody knew our family. Nobody stared when they saw us talking with our hands. But in the new town, people did stare. Of course, they pretended they didn't see us. That was dumb. I knew they were looking.

It was even worse when my mom and dad talked. It seemed as if everyone looked at us when they heard my parents' strange-sounding voices. Sometimes Gina and I felt embarrassed, especially when we had to tell someone what my mother or father had said.

Gina and I didn't want to feel that way. We knew how shy my parents felt. We knew mom missed her art classes. We knew they both missed their old friends. We knew they were as lonesome and homesick as we were!

One awful day I saw three kids making fun of my parents. They were standing behind Mom and Dad and pretending to talk with their hands. I was so upset I wanted to pretend something, too. Just for a minute, I wanted to pretend my mother and father were not my parents. I had never felt that way before.

I was really so ashamed of myself.

That very same day Gina's favorite teacher gave her a note to take home. It was an invitation for our family to go to a performance of the National Theatre of the Deaf.

At first, I didn't want to give the invitation to my parents. I didn't want them to go. I didn't want people to make fun of them or feel sorry for Gina and me.

But Gina said they should go. She said that the play would be in sign language, and who would understand it better than our parents? I knew she was right. Besides, Mom and Dad needed to go out and meet new people.

Still, I was worried about what might happen. The night of the play, all sorts of questions were popping into my mind as I dragged up the steps into the hall. Then I saw those three dumb kids standing in the doorway. One of them grinned and wiggled his fingers at me.

That made me angry! I wanted to give him a good punch in the nose, but I kept going.

The big hall was filled with people. Just inside the door, my mother signed to me, "Where will we sit?"

To our surprise, a man stood up and said, "There are five seats over here."

We couldn't believe it. He was talking in sign language!

All around us, people were laughing and talking. Many of them were talking with their hands. They didn't seem to care who was watching.

Before the play started, we learned from our program that some of the actors were deaf and some could hear. The hearing actors and some of the deaf actors would speak in the play. All of the actors would sign, sometimes for themselves and sometimes for each other. And sometimes they would all sign together. Everyone in the audience would be able to understand what was going on.

The play we saw was called *The Wooden Boy*. It was about Pinocchio, a puppet who wanted to be a real boy. It was both funny and sad.

After the play, we went backstage to meet the actors. The deaf performers talked with people who knew sign language. The hearing actors helped the other people understand what was being said.

I was proud of my parents. They were smiling, and their fingers were flying as fast as anyone's. For the first time in many months, they seemed to feel at home.

Then we had another surprise. Gina's teacher came over to us. She talked very slowly and carefully so my mother could read her lips. Then she signed with her hands!

Gina was excited. Her favorite teacher, who wasn't deaf, had words in her hands, too. Gina was learning something she didn't know before. We all were. We were learning there were many friendly people in our new town who could talk with our parents. I decided this place wasn't going to be so bad, after all.

I think some of the hearing people around us were learning something too—even those awful kids, who were still following us around.

Maybe they never thought about it before, but being deaf doesn't mean you can't hear or talk. If you have to, you can hear with your eyes and talk with your hands.

I'm glad that Gina and Diane and I know so many signs already. Why don't you learn a few yourself?

Reader's Response ∼ How would you feel if you saw people making fun of your parents the way Michael did?

Library Link ∼ *An interesting book about sign language is* A Show of Hands *by Mary Beth Sullivan and Linda Bourke.*

Friendly Signs

Many people learn sign language because they are deaf or because they know someone who is deaf—or just because it is a lot of fun. You can send a secret message to a friend across a noisy room, "talk" silently in the library, or even learn to sign a familiar song like the one below. Most of all, you can learn the language of thousands of deaf people in the United States.

Quick Facts

English, Spanish, and Italian are the three most common languages used to communicate in the United States. Do you know what another important language is? It's American Sign Language.

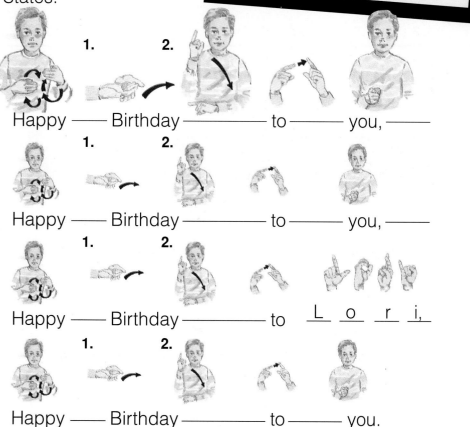

Happy —— Birthday —————— to ——— you, ———

Happy —— Birthday —————— to ——— you, ———

Happy —— Birthday —————— to   L o r i,

Happy —— Birthday —————— to ——— you.

SPORTS SIGNALS

by Gary Apple

Imagine that you are the coach of a football team. Your team is behind by one point, and there is time for only one more play. The other team expects you to throw a long pass, but you decide to surprise them and run with the ball.

How do you communicate your plan to your players? You can't shout, "Surprise them by running instead of passing!" Your players may not hear you, and if they do, the other team will hear you, too. The surprise will be lost.

Can you tell which of these coaches is giving a signal?

Instead, you communicate by giving your team a secret signal using sign language. Before the game, you tell your team that if you put both hands on your head, it means to run with the ball. Your players read your signal and try to run with the ball. Success! Your team scores, and you win the game!

Sign language is used all the time in sports. Coaches signal players. Players signal other players. Officials signal players, and players signal officials. Everyone signals everybody!

Of course, signals aren't used only for secret plays. In football, for example, before a player catches a punt, he can wave his hand to signal a *fair catch*. With this signal the player makes a deal with the other team. It means, "If you don't try to tackle me, I won't try to run with the ball when I catch it."

Another sports signal that everyone understands and uses is the "time-out" sign. This is done by making a letter "T" with the hands. It tells the official to stop the clock. Football and basketball are two of the sports that use this sign.

Fair Catch!   **Time Out!**   **Safe!**

How many secret signals can you find in this picture?

Secret signals are used when one team doesn't want the other team to know what's going on. If you have ever watched a football game, you may have noticed a coach on the sidelines making strange movements. What he is doing is giving secret directions to the players on the field.

Football coaches can be very tricky. Sometimes, two coaches on the same team give signals at the same time. One coach gives the real secret play while the other gives signals that the players ignore. This is done to confuse the other team, so they don't know which signal is the real signal.

Baseball is the sport in which secret signals are used the most. When you watch a baseball game, it might look like the players are just waiting around for the next pitch. If you look closer, however, you will see that secret communications are being sent all over the field. If you see a player scratch his chin or a coach push his cap back on his head, there is a good chance that you have just seen a secret signal.

The catcher is about to signal for a certain type of pitch.

The pitcher and the catcher use sign language before every pitch. The catcher gives a sign to tell the pitcher the kind of pitch to throw. One finger may mean "Throw a fastball." Two fingers may mean "Pitch a curve ball." The catcher also uses a sign to tell the pitcher where to throw the pitch: inside, outside, high, or low. If the pitcher doesn't agree with the catcher, he will shake his head. The catcher will then secretly suggest another pitch.

Before every game, the catcher and the pitcher must talk about the sign language to be used. This way, there will be no mistakes. If a pitcher does not understand the signs, he might throw the wrong pitch, and the catcher may not be able to catch the ball.

The pitcher isn't the only one watching the catcher's secret signs. The second baseman and the shortstop also follow the sign language. If they know the kind of pitch to expect, they can guess where the ball will go if the batter hits it. The shortstop and second baseman have a set of secret signs of their own. They use them to tell the outfielders, who are far away and can't see the catcher, what kind of pitch is on the way. When a shortstop puts his hands on his knees, he might be telling the outfielders to expect a fastball.

The team that is up to bat also uses secret sign language. During a ballgame, coaches stand near first base and third base. Part of their job is to give secret directions to the batter. They also direct the runners who have reached a base. These coaches may seem to be just standing around, but don't be fooled. When they dust off their sleeve or hold their elbow, they may be telling the batter to bunt or the base runner to steal a base.

A base coach secretly signals batters and base runners.

Teams are always trying to find out what the other team's signals are. To stop this from happening, teams often change their signals during a game. A sign that meant "steal the base" in one inning may mean "stay on base" in another. Coaches can get even trickier than that. For example, base runners might be told to ignore all signs unless the coach's feet are in a certain position.

The next time you're at the ballpark or stadium, pay attention to the movements of the team members. See if you can tell which are secret signals and which are everyday movements. Players and coaches can be tricky, so watch carefully; but don't be too suspicious. When a coach scratches his chin, he might just have an itch!

Reader's Response ∽ Do you think understanding sports signals will help you enjoy sports more? Why or why not?

Library Link ∽ *If you would like to learn more about signals, you might enjoy reading* Train Whistles *by Helen Roney Sattler.*

THE PERFECT PITCH

YOGI BERRA
NEW YORK YANKEES
CATCHER

A catcher has to be one of the smartest players on a baseball team. He leads the team's defense. As you know, his biggest job is to signal the pitcher which pitches to throw and where to throw them. But how does he decide?

Before the game the catcher thinks about which pitches his pitcher is throwing well and which ones he is having trouble getting over the plate. Next he studies the records of the batters on the opposing team to learn which pitches each batter likes to hit. During the game he uses this information to choose the right pitches.

The catcher also has to think about what has already happened in the game. Is there anyone on base? Are there any outs yet? As you can see, it's not a simple process to choose the right pitches!

These cards show three of baseball's best catchers. Whose card would you like to add?

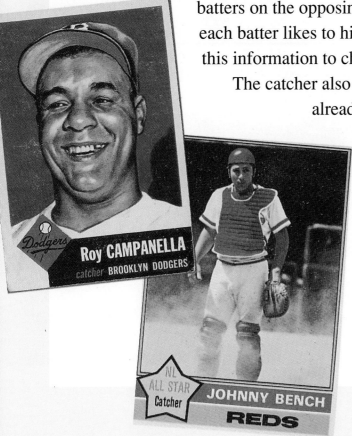

Roy CAMPANELLA
catcher BROOKLYN DODGERS

NL ALL STAR Catcher JOHNNY BENCH
REDS

MUFARO'S *Beautiful* DAUGHTERS

AN AFRICAN TALE

*written and
illustrated by
John Steptoe*

A long time ago, in a certain place in Africa, a small village lay across a river and half a day's journey from a city where a great king lived. A man named Mufaro lived in this village with his two daughters, who were called Manyara and Nyasha. Everyone agreed that Manyara and Nyasha were very beautiful.

111

Manyara was almost always in a bad temper. She teased her sister whenever their father's back was turned, and she had been heard to say, "Someday, Nyasha, I will be a queen, and you will be a servant in my household."

"If that should come to pass," Nyasha responded, "I will be pleased to serve you. But why do you say such things? You are clever and strong and beautiful. Why are you so unhappy?"

"Because everyone talks about how kind *you* are, and they praise everything you do," Manyara replied. "I'm certain that Father loves you best. But when I am a queen, everyone will know that your silly kindness is only weakness."

Nyasha was sad that Manyara felt this way, but she ignored her sister's words and went about her chores. Nyasha kept a small plot of land, on which she grew millet, sunflowers, yams, and vegetables. She always sang as she worked, and some said it was her singing that made her crops more bountiful than anyone else's.

One day, Nyasha noticed a small garden snake resting beneath a yam vine. "Good day, little Nyoka," she called to him. "You are welcome here. You will keep away any creatures who might spoil my vegetables." She bent forward, gave the little snake a loving pat on the head, and then returned to her work.

113

From that day on, Nyoka was always at Nyasha's side when she tended her garden. It was said that she sang all the more sweetly when he was there.

Mufaro knew nothing of how Manyara treated Nyasha. Nyasha was too considerate of her father's feelings to complain, and Manyara was always careful to behave herself when Mufaro was around.

Early one morning, a messenger from the city arrived. The Great King wanted a wife. "The Most Worthy and Beautiful Daughters in the Land are invited to appear before the King, and he will choose one to become Queen!" the messenger proclaimed.

Mufaro called Manyara and Nyasha to him. "It would be a great honor to have one of you chosen," he said. "Prepare yourselves to journey to the city. I will call together all our friends to make a wedding party. We will leave tomorrow as the sun rises."

"But, my father," Manyara said sweetly, "it would be painful for either of us to leave you, even to be wife to the king. I know Nyasha would grieve to death if she were parted from you. I am strong. Send me to the city, and let poor Nyasha be happy here with you."

Mufaro beamed with pride. "The king has asked for the most worthy and the most beautiful. No, Manyara, I cannot send you alone. Only a king can choose between two such worthy daughters. Both of you must go!"

That night, when everyone was asleep, Manyara stole quietly out of the village. She had never been in the forest at night before, and she was frightened, but her greed to be the first to appear before the king drove her on. In her hurry, she almost stumbled over a small boy who suddenly appeared, standing in the path.

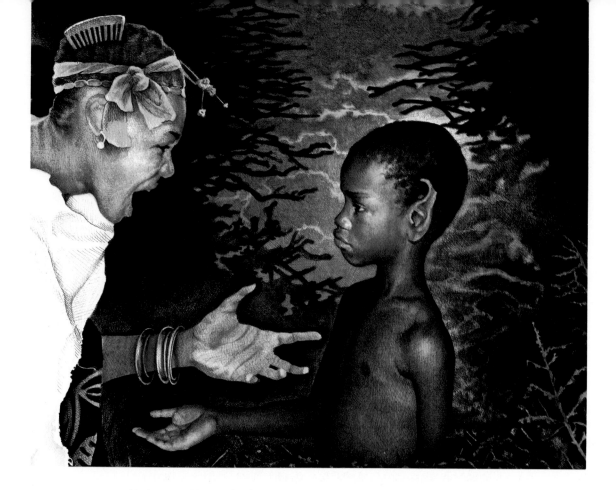

"Please," said the boy. "I am hungry. Will you give me something to eat?"

"I have brought only enough for myself," Manyara replied.

"But, please!" said the boy. "I am so *very* hungry."

"Out of my way, boy! Tomorrow I will become your queen. How dare you stand in my path?"

After traveling for what seemed to be a great distance, Manyara came to a small clearing. There, silhouetted against the moonlight, was an old woman seated on a large stone.

The old woman spoke. "I will give you some advice, Manyara. Soon after you pass the place where two paths cross, you will see a grove of trees. They will laugh at you. You must not laugh in return. Later, you will meet a man with his head under his arm. You must be polite to him."

"How do you know my name? How dare you advise your future queen? Stand aside, you ugly old woman!" Manyara scolded, and then rushed on her way without looking back.

Just as the old woman had foretold, Manyara came to a grove of trees, and they did indeed seem to be laughing at her.

"I must be calm," Manyara thought. "I will *not* be frightened." She looked up at the trees and laughed out loud. "I laugh at you, trees!" she shouted, and she hurried on.

It was not yet dawn when Manyara heard the sound of rushing water. "The river must be up ahead," she thought. "The great city is just on the other side."

But there, on the rise, she saw a man with his head tucked under his arm. Manyara ran past him without speaking. "A queen acknowledges only those who please her," she said to herself. "I will be queen. I will be queen," she chanted, as she hurried on toward the city.

Nyasha woke at the first light of dawn. As she put on her finest garments, she thought how her life might be changed forever beyond this day. "I'd much prefer to live here," she admitted to herself. "I'd hate to leave this village and never see my father or sing to little Nyoka again."

Her thoughts were interrupted by loud shouts and a commotion from the wedding party assembled outside. Manyara was missing! Everyone bustled about, searching and calling for her. When they found her footprints on the path that led to the city, they decided to go on as planned.

As the wedding party moved through the forest, brightly plumed birds darted about in the cool green shadows beneath the trees. Though anxious about her sister, Nyasha was soon filled with excitement about all there was to see.

They were deep in the forest when she saw the small boy standing by the side of the path.

"You must be hungry," she said, and handed him a yam she had brought for her lunch. The boy smiled and disappeared as quietly as he had come.

Later, as they were approaching the place where the two paths crossed, the old woman appeared and silently pointed the way to the city. Nyasha thanked her and gave her a small pouch filled with sunflower seeds.

The sun was high in the sky when the party came to the grove of towering trees. Their uppermost branches seemed to bow down to Nyasha as she passed beneath them.

At last, someone announced that they were near their destination.

Nyasha ran ahead and topped the rise before the others could catch up with her. She stood transfixed at her first sight of the city. "Oh, my father," she called. "A great spirit must stand guard here! Just look at what lies before us. I never in all my life dreamed there could be anything so beautiful!"

Arm in arm, Nyasha and her father descended the hill, crossed the river, and approached the city gate. Just as they entered through the great doors, the air was rent by piercing cries, and Manyara ran wildly out of a chamber at the center of the enclosure. When she saw Nyasha, she fell upon her, sobbing.

"Do not go to the king, my sister. Oh, please, Father, do not let her go!" she cried hysterically. "There's a great monster there, a snake with five heads! He said that he knew all my faults and that I displeased him. He would have swallowed me alive if I had not run. Oh, my sister, please do not go inside that place."

It frightened Nyasha to see her sister so upset. But, leaving her father to comfort Manyara, she bravely made her way to the chamber and opened the door.

On the seat of the great chief's stool lay the little garden snake. Nyasha laughed with relief and joy.

"My little friend!" she exclaimed. "It's such a pleasure to see you, but why are you here?"

"I am the king," Nyoka replied.

And there, before Nyasha's eyes, the garden snake changed shape.

"I am the king. I am also the hungry boy with whom you shared a yam in the forest and the old woman to whom you made a gift of sunflower seeds. But you know me best as Nyoka. Because I have been all of these, I know you to be the Most Worthy and Most Beautiful Daughter in the Land. It would make me very happy if you would be my wife."

And so it was that, a long time ago, Nyasha agreed to be married. The king's mother and sisters took Nyasha to their house, and the wedding preparations began. The best weavers in the land laid out their finest cloth for her wedding garments. Villagers from all around were invited to the celebration, and a great feast was held. Nyasha prepared the bread for the wedding feast from millet that had been brought from her village.

Mufaro proclaimed to all who would hear him that he was the happiest father in all the land, for he was blessed with two beautiful and worthy daughters— Nyasha, the queen; and Manyara, a servant in the queen's household.

Reader's Response ∼ The pictures in this story are interesting and beautiful. Which one is your favorite? Why did you choose it?

Library Link ∼ *If you enjoyed reading this story by John Steptoe, you might like to read other books by this author, such as* Train Ride *and* The Story of Jumping Mouse.

JOHN *Steptoe*

John Steptoe was sixteen years old when he wrote and illustrated his first children's book, *Stevie*. It's a story about a young boy's efforts to overcome jealousy. The book was first printed in *Life* magazine and made Mr. Steptoe famous.

It took John Steptoe two and one-half years to write and illustrate *Mufaro's Beautiful Daughters*.

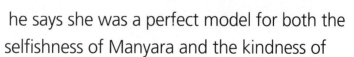

He used his daughter Bweela as a model for both sisters. She was sixteen at the time and he says she was a perfect model for both the selfishness of Manyara and the kindness of Nyasha. He chose the story because he wanted to create a book that would tell children some of the things that even he had not known about his ancestors in Africa.

123

And My Heart Soars

The beauty of the trees,
The softness of the air,
The fragrance of the grass,
　　speaks to me.

The summit of the mountain,
The thunder of the sky,
The rhythm of the sea,
　　speaks to me.

The faintness of the stars,
The freshness of the morning,
The dew drop on the flower,
　　speaks to me.

The strength of fire,
The taste of salmon,
The trail of the sun,
And the life that never goes away,
　　They speak to me.

And my heart soars.

— Chief Dan George

Eagle Flight

An eagle wings gracefully
   through the sky.
On the earth I stand
   and watch.
My heart flies with it.

— Alonzo Lopez

125

The Boy Who Cried WOLF

by Genie Iverson
from the fable by Aesop

Characters: Storyteller   Little Girl
               Shepherd Boy   First Farmhand
               Father   Second Farmhand
               Old Woman   Third Farmhand
               Farmer

ACT ONE

Storyteller: A shepherd boy and his father stand talking on a hillside. Their sheep move about them.

Father: Are you ready to look after these sheep by yourself, son? It's time for me to go back to the village.

Shepherd Boy: (*uncertain*) I think so, Papa.

Father: I'll help you herd our sheep here each morning. And I'll come back at sunset to help you drive them home. But you must stay with them during the day.

Shepherd Boy: Yes, Papa. Only . . . (*looking around*) . . . I don't think I'll like being up here alone.

Father: Alone? Nonsense! Look down there at the road. People come and go all day.

Shepherd Boy: But they never stop.

Father: Maybe they don't stop. But they will come if you ever need help. Just call. (*handing boy the crook*) I have to go now. But I'll be back at sunset. (Father *leaves and the shepherd sits down to watch his sheep.*)

Storyteller: Slowly—very slowly the morning passes. The young shepherd boy feels more and more alone.

Shepherd Boy: I don't like staying here all day by myself. (*sighs*) It's lonely here.

Storyteller: Looking down the hill, the shepherd boy sees an old woman walking along the road. Pails of milk swing from a pole across her shoulders.

Shepherd Boy: I wish that old woman would stop and visit. I wish . . . (*pause*) . . . I know what I'll do! (*leaps up waving his crook*) Help! Help! A WOLF is after my sheep!

Storyteller: The old woman hurries up the hill to help. Milk splashes from her pails.

Old Woman: (*winded*) Where? . . . Where is the wolf? We can chase him with my pole!

Shepherd Boy: (*looking down*) There is no wolf. I wanted you to stop and visit. So I played a trick on you.

Old Woman: No wolf! You mean you made me run up this hill for nothing? What is the matter with you, boy?

Shepherd Boy: I didn't mean any harm.

Old Woman: (*picking up her pails*) Hummf! Just look at these pails! Empty! All that good milk . . . spilled for nothing.

Shepherd Boy: I just wanted you to stop and visit. . . .

Old Woman: Tricking folks is a sorry business. I came to visit you today, but trouble may be your visitor tomorrow. Mark my words. (*walking away muttering*) He'll be sorry . . . sorry indeed. Just wait and see!

ACT TWO

Storyteller: It is the next morning. The unhappy shepherd boy sits on the hillside. As his sheep move about him, he thinks about the long, lonely day ahead.

Shepherd Boy: (*wearily*) Nibble . . . Nibble . . . Nibble!

Baaaa! . . . Baaaa! . . . Baaaa!

Nibble . . . Baaaa!

Baaaa! . . . Nibble! (*long sigh*)

All day long . . . that's all you old sheep ever do!

Storyteller: The shepherd boy hears the rumble of a cart.

Shepherd Boy: Listen! Someone's coming! (*stands and looks down the hill*)

Storyteller: A farmer and his little girl appear on the road, pulling a cart filled with turnips.

Shepherd Boy: Do I dare call out again that there is a wolf? If I do . . . maybe they'll stop. . . . (*pause*) . . . Help! Help! A wolf is after my sheep!

Storyteller: The farmer leaves his cart and runs up the hill to help. His little girl hurries along behind.

Farmer: Where? Where's the wolf?

Little Girl: (*afraid*) Is the wolf hiding behind that tree? Will he eat me?

Farmer: I don't see any wolf. (*looking around*) There's no wolf here!

Shepherd Boy: It was just a trick.

Farmer: (*angrily*) You called for help when you didn't need it! Shame on you!

Shepherd Boy: Please don't be angry. I get lonely sitting here all day by myself.

Farmer: (*taking* Little Girl *by hand*) Come along, child. This boy has wasted enough of our time with his tricks. But someday he'll be sorry.

Little Girl: (*as they walk away*) Why will he be sorry, Papa?

Farmer: Because tricks bring trouble. Just wait and see. What that boy did today will be remembered tomorrow. (*They exit.*)

ACT THREE
(Scene One)

Storyteller: It is another bright, cool morning. The shepherd boy has watched his flock since sunrise. He is bored and lonely.

Shepherd Boy: Same old hillside! (*sigh*) Same old sheep! Same old grass! And the sun is not even overhead yet. It's still morning! (*long sigh*) Maybe I'll sit and watch the road. Somebody should be coming along soon.

Storyteller: The shepherd boy is about to sit when he hears a loud growl. He turns. A wolf is crouched near his flock.

Shepherd Boy: A WOLF! (*He crawls behind a rock and peeks out.*) A REAL wolf! What can I do!

Storyteller: As the wolf creeps nearer to the frightened sheep, singing is heard from the road below.

Farmhands: (*offstage*) Hey, ho! Hey, ho!
It's to the fields we go,
With hoe and rake,
With rake and hoe,
Hey, ho! Hey, ho!

Storyteller: Three farmhands come into view. The shepherd boy runs to the top of the hill shouting.

Shepherd Boy: (*waving his crook*) HELP! HELP! A WOLF is after my sheep!

First Farmhand: (*stopping*) Look. It's that shepherd boy! The one folks are talking about.

Second Farmhand: They say he cries "wolf" when there is no wolf.

Third Farmhand: (*nodding*) Foolish boy! You can't believe a word he says.

Shepherd Boy: (*calling as loudly as he can*) Hurry! Hurry! The wolf is taking my sheep!

First Farmhand: (*calling to shepherd*) We DON'T believe you!

Second Farmhand: That's right! We've heard about you and your tricks.

Third Farmhand: You can't fool us! We know there is no wolf! (*The farmhands walk away laughing.*)

Shepherd Boy: Come back! Come back! This ISN'T a trick. This time there IS a wolf! A REAL wolf! . . . (*sobs*) . . . He is running away with my sheep. (*The boy sits down, covers his face with his hands and cries.*)

(Scene Two)

Storyteller: It is sunset. The shepherd sits with his head in his hands. The wolf is gone. But so are some of the sheep. Father approaches.

Father: Are you ready to take the sheep home?

Shepherd Boy: Oh yes, Papa! But some of the sheep are gone! A wolf came—a great big wolf!

Father: A wolf! Did you call for help?

Shepherd Boy: Yes, Papa. Yes. There were men on the road. I called. But they wouldn't come. (*lowering his eyes*) They thought that I was playing a trick.

Father: (*puzzled*) A trick?

Shepherd Boy: (*hanging his head*) Before when I was lonely, I cried "wolf" so that people would stop and visit. Then . . . then there really was a wolf. And I called. But they didn't believe me.

Father: (*sitting down on a rock*) Well . . . have you learned something?

Shepherd Boy: (*sitting down beside his father*) Yes, Papa. I learned that I should always tell the truth . . . (*pause*) . . . because if I don't, people won't believe me when I do.

THE END

Reader's Response ∿ Were you surprised that the boy's father didn't punish him for losing the sheep? What would you have done?

Library Link ∿ *If you enjoyed this play based on a tale by Aesop, you might want to read* Aesop's Fables, *edited by Anne White, or* Tales from Aesop, *edited by Harold Jones.*

Never Cry Wolf

Why are *Little Red Riding Hood*, *Peter and the Wolf*, and *The Boy Who Cried Wolf* alike? They are all stories about big, bad wolves.

Have you ever read a story about big, **good** wolves? Farley Mowat is a scientist who once studied wolves in northern Canada. He wrote a book called *Never Cry Wolf* about his experiences. He said that he "came to know and respect the wolves as friends." Here are some things he learned about them:

They can communicate with each other over long distances. Yips, howls, growls, and barks all mean different things.

Wolves are good parents. When the mother and father wolf go hunting, another member of the pack will babysit the pups.

Wolves don't hunt for fun. They only hunt when they are hungry.

When there is plenty to eat, wolves have more pups. When food is scarce, they have fewer.

What kind of story would you write about wolves?

In Which Piglet Meets a Heffalump

from
Winnie-the-Pooh

At first as they stumped along the path which edged the Hundred Acre Wood, they didn't say much to each other; but when they came to the stream and had helped each other across the stepping stones, and were able to walk side by side again over the heather, they began to talk in a friendly way about this and that, and Piglet said, "If you see what I mean, Pooh," and Pooh said, "It's just what I think myself, Piglet," and Piglet said, "But, on the other hand, Pooh, we must remember," and Pooh said, "Quite true, Piglet, although I had forgotten it for the moment." And then, just as they came to the Six Pine Trees, Pooh looked round to see that nobody else was listening, and said in a very solemn voice:

"Piglet, I have decided something."

"What have you decided, Pooh?"

"I have decided to catch a Heffalump."

Pooh nodded his head several times as he said this, and waited for Piglet to say "How?" or "Pooh, you couldn't!" or something helpful of that sort, but Piglet said nothing. The fact was Piglet was wishing that *he* had thought about it first.

"I shall do it," said Pooh, after waiting a little longer, "by means of a trap. And it must be a Cunning Trap, so you will have to help me, Piglet."

"Pooh," said Piglet, feeling quite happy again now, "I will." And then he said, "How shall we do it?" and Pooh said, "That's just it. How?" And then they sat down together to think it out.

Pooh's first idea was that they should dig a Very Deep Pit, and then the Heffalump would come along and fall into the Pit, and——

"Why?" said Piglet.

"Why what?" said Pooh.

"Why would he fall in?"

Pooh rubbed his nose with his paw, and said that the Heffalump might be walking along, humming a little song, and looking up at the sky, wondering if it would rain, and so he wouldn't see the Very Deep Pit until he was half-way down, when it would be too late.

Piglet said that this was a very good Trap, but supposing it were raining already?

Pooh rubbed his nose again, and said that he hadn't thought of that. And then he brightened up, and said that, if it were raining already, the Heffalump

would be looking at the sky wondering if it would *clear up,* and so he wouldn't see the Very Deep Pit until he was half-way down. . . . When it would be too late.

Piglet said that, now that this point had been explained, he thought it was a Cunning Trap.

Pooh was very proud when he heard this, and he felt that the Heffalump was as good as caught already, but there was just one other thing which had to be thought about, and it was this. *Where should they dig the Very Deep Pit?*

Piglet said that the best place would be somewhere where a Heffalump was, just before he fell into it, only about a foot farther on.

"But then he would see us digging it," said Pooh.

"Not if he was looking at the sky."

"He would Suspect," said Pooh, "if he happened to look down." He thought for a long time and then added sadly, "It isn't as easy as I thought. I suppose that's why Heffalumps hardly *ever* get caught."

"That must be it," said Piglet.

They sighed and got up; and when they had taken a few gorse prickles out of themselves they sat down again; and all the time Pooh was saying to himself, "If only I could *think* of something!" For he felt sure that a Very Clever Brain could catch a Heffalump if only he knew the right way to go about it.

"Suppose," he said to Piglet, "*you* wanted to catch *me*, how would you do it?"

"Well," said Piglet, "I should do it like this. I should make a Trap, and I should put a Jar of Honey in the Trap, and you would smell it, and you would go in after it, and——"

"And I would go in after it," said Pooh excitedly, "only very carefully so as not to hurt myself, and I would get to the Jar of Honey, and I should lick round the edges first of all, pretending that there wasn't any more, you know, and then I should walk away and think about it a little, and then I should come back and start licking in the middle of the jar, and then——"

"Yes, well never mind about that. There you would be, and there I should catch you. Now the first thing to think of is, What do Heffalumps like? I should think acorns, shouldn't you? We'll get a lot of—I say, wake up, Pooh!"

Pooh, who had gone into a happy dream, woke up with a start, and said that Honey was a much more trappy thing than Haycorns. Piglet didn't think so; and they were just going to argue about it, when Piglet remembered that, if they put acorns in the Trap, *he* would have to find the acorns, but if they put honey, then Pooh would have to give up some of his own honey, so he said, "All right, honey then," just as Pooh remembered it too, and was going to say, "All right, haycorns."

"Honey," said Piglet to himself in a thoughtful way, as if it were now settled. "*I'll* dig the pit, while *you* go and get the honey."

"Very well," said Pooh, and he stumped off.

As soon as he got home, he went to the larder; and he stood on a chair, and took down a very large

jar of honey from the top shelf. It had HUNNY written on it, but, just to make sure, he took off the paper cover and looked at it, and it *looked* just like honey. "But you never can tell," said Pooh. "I remember my uncle saying once that he had seen cheese just this colour." So he put his tongue in, and took a large lick. "Yes," he said, "it is. No doubt about that. And honey, I should say, right down to the bottom of the jar. Unless, of course," he said, "somebody put cheese in at the bottom just for a joke. Perhaps I had better go a *little* further . . . just in case . . . in case Heffalumps *don't* like cheese . . . same as me. . . . Ah!" And he gave a deep sigh. "I *was* right. It *is* honey, right the way down."

Having made certain of this, he took the jar back to Piglet, and Piglet looked up from the bottom of his Very Deep Pit, and said, "Got it?" and Pooh said, "Yes, but it isn't quite a full jar," and he threw it down to Piglet, and Piglet said, "No, it isn't! Is that all you've got left?" and Pooh said "Yes." Because it was. So Piglet put the jar at the bottom of the Pit, and climbed out, and they went off home together.

"Well, good night, Pooh," said Piglet, when they had got to Pooh's house. "And we meet at six o'clock tomorrow morning by the Pine Trees, and see how many Heffalumps we've got in our Trap."

"Six o'clock, Piglet. And have you got any string?"

"No. Why do you want string?"

"To lead them home with."

"Oh! . . . I *think* Heffalumps come if you whistle."

The Sun was still in bed, but there was a lightness in the sky over the Hundred Acre Wood which seemed to show that it was waking up and would soon be kicking off the clothes. In the half-light the Pine Trees looked cold and lonely, and the Very Deep Pit seemed deeper than it was, and Pooh's jar of honey at the bottom was something mysterious, a shape and no more. But as he got nearer to it his nose told him that it was indeed honey, and his tongue came out and began to polish up his mouth, ready for it.

"Bother!" said Pooh, as he got his nose inside the jar. "A Heffalump has been eating it!" And then he thought a little and said, "Oh, no, *I* did. I forgot."

Indeed, he had eaten most of it. But there was a little left at the very bottom of the jar, and he pushed his head right in, and began to lick. . . .

By and by Piglet woke up. As soon as he woke he said to himself, "Oh!" Then he said bravely, "Yes," and then, still more bravely, "Quite so." But he didn't feel very brave, for the word which was really jiggeting about in his brain was "Heffalumps."

What was a Heffalump like?

Was it Fierce?

Did it come when you whistled? And *how* did it come?

Was it Fond of Pigs at all?

If it was Fond of Pigs, did it make any difference *what sort of Pig?*

Supposing it was Fierce with Pigs, would it make any difference *if the Pig had a grandfather called TRESPASSERS WILLIAM?*

He didn't know the answer to any of these questions . . . and he was going to see his first Heffalump in about an hour from now!

Of course Pooh would be with him, and it was much more Friendly with two. But suppose Heffalumps were Very Fierce with Pigs *and* Bears? Wouldn't it be better to pretend that he had a headache, and couldn't go up to the Six Pine Trees this morning? But then suppose that it was a very fine day, and there was no Heffalump in the trap, here he would be, in bed all the morning, simply wasting his time for nothing. What should he do?

And then he had a Clever Idea. He would go up very quietly to the Six Pine Trees now, peep cautiously into the Trap, and see if there *was* Heffalump there. And if there was, he would go to bed, and if there wasn't, he wouldn't.

So off he went. At first he thought that there wouldn't be a Heffalump in the Trap, and then he thought that there would, and as he got nearer he was *sure* that there would, because he could hear it heffalumping about it like anything.

"Oh, dear, oh, dear, oh, dear!" said Piglet to himself. And he wanted to run away. But somehow, having got so near, he felt that he must just see what a Heffalump was like. So he crept to the side of the Trap and looked in. . . .

And all the time Winnie-the-Pooh had been trying to get the honey-jar off his head. The more he shook it, the more tightly it stuck. *"Bother!"* he said, inside the jar, and *"Oh, help!"* and, mostly *"Ow!"* And he tried bumping it against things, but as he couldn't see what he was bumping it against, it didn't help him; and he tried to climb out of the Trap, but as he could see nothing but jar, and not much of that, he couldn't find his way. So at last he lifted up his head, jar and all, and made a loud, roaring noise of Sadness and Despair . . . and it was at that moment that Piglet looked down.

"Help, help!" cried Piglet, "a Heffalump, a Horrible Heffalump!" and he scampered off as hard as he could, still crying out, "Help, help, a Herrible Hoffalump! Hoff, Hoff, a Hellible Horralump! Holl, Holl, a Hoffable Hellerump!" And he didn't stop crying and scampering until he got to Christopher Robin's house.

"Whatever's the matter, Piglet?" said Christopher Robin, who was just getting up.

"Heff," said Piglet, breathing so hard that he could hardly speak, "a Hell—a Heff—a Heffalump."

"Where?"

"Up there," said Piglet, waving his paw.

"What did it look like?"

"Like—like——It had the biggest head you ever saw, Christopher Robin. A great enormous thing, like—like nothing. A huge big—well, like a—I don't know—like an enormous big nothing. Like a jar."

"Well," said Christopher Robin, putting on his shoes, "I shall go and look at it. Come on."

Piglet wasn't afraid if he had Christopher Robin with him, so off they went. . . .

"I can hear it, can't you?" said Piglet anxiously, as they got near.

"I can hear *something*," said Christopher Robin.

It was Pooh bumping his head against a tree-root he had found.

"There!" said Piglet. "Isn't it *awful?*" And he held on tight to Christopher Robin's hand.

Suddenly Christopher Robin began to laugh . . . and he laughed . . . and he laughed . . . and he laughed. And while he was still laughing—*Crash* went the Heffalump's head against the tree-root, Smash went the jar, and out came Pooh's head again. . . .

Then Piglet saw what a Foolish Piglet he had been, and he was so ashamed of himself that he ran straight off home and went to bed with a headache. But Christopher Robin and Pooh went home to breakfast together.

"Oh, Bear!" said Christopher Robin. "How I do love you!"

"So do I," said Pooh.

Reader's Response ∼ What was the funniest part of this story? What made it funny to you?

Library Link ∼ *This story was taken from the book* Winnie-the-Pooh. *You might enjoy reading the entire book to learn more about Pooh and his friends and all the fun they have together.*

GLOSSARY

Full pronunciation key* The pronunciation of each word is shown just after the word, in this way: **abbreviate** (ə brē′vē āt).

The letters and signs used are pronounced as in the words below.

The mark ′ is placed after a syllable with a primary or heavy accent as in the example above.

The mark ′ after a syllable shows a secondary or lighter accent, as in **abbreviation** (ə brē′vē ā′shən).

SYMBOL	KEY WORDS	SYMBOL	KEY WORDS	SYMBOL	KEY WORDS
a	ask, fat	u	up, cut	r	red, dear
ā	ape, date	ur	fur, fern	s	sell, pass
ä	car, father			t	top, hat
		ə	a in ago	v	vat, have
e	elf, ten		e in agent	w	will, always
er	berry, care		e in father	y	yet, yard
ē	even, meet		i in unity	z	zebra, haze
			o in collect		
i	is, hit		u in focus	ch	chin, arch
ir	mirror, here			ŋ	ring, singer
ī	ice, fire	b	bed, dub	sh	she, dash
		d	did, had	th	thin, truth
o	lot, pond	f	fall, off	*th*	then, father
ō	open, go	g	get, dog	zh	s in pleasure
ô	law, horn	h	he, ahead		
oi	oil, point	j	joy, jump	′	as in (ā′b′l)
o͝o	look, pull	k	kill, bake		
o͞o	ooze, tool	l	let, ball		
yo͞o	unite, cure	m	met, trim		
yo͞o	cute, few	n	not, ton		
ou	out, crowd	p	put, tap		

*Pronunciation key and respellings adapted from *Webster's New World Dictionary, Basic School Edition,* Copyright © 1983 by Simon & Schuster, Inc. Reprinted by permission.

A

ab·so·lute·ly (ab′sə lo͞ot lē)
adverb. completely; perfectly.

ac·tor (ak′tər) *noun.* a person
who performs in plays, in
movies, or on television.
actors.

ad·vice (əd vīs′) *noun.* an
opinion given about what
action to take or about how
to do something.

al·pha·bet (al′fə bet) *noun.*
1. the letters of a language
placed in order. **2.** a system
of symbols that are used in
communicating, such as the
Braille alphabet for the blind.

an·ces·tor (an′ses tər) *noun.*
1. a person from an earlier
generation in the same family
line, especially someone
earlier than a grandparent; a
forefather: The traditions
were passed down for
hundreds of years by our
ancestors. **2.** an early kind of
animal from which later
kinds developed. **ancestors.**

an·nounce (ə no͞uns′) *verb.*
1. to say or tell something
to an audience. **2.** to make
something known to others:
He *announced* that the class
would take a trip to the
museum. **3.** to say or tell.
announced.

at·ten·tion (ə ten′shən) *noun.*
the ability to keep your mind
or thoughts on something;
notice.

B

bal·let (bal′ā *or* ba lā′) *noun.*
a dance that tells a story
through a series of planned,
graceful movements usually
performed by dancers
wearing costumes.

bore (bôr) *verb.* to tire by
being dull or uninteresting.
—**boring** *adjective.* dull,
uninteresting.

bor·row (bor′ō *or* bôr′ō) *verb.*
1. to use something that
belongs to someone else
after agreeing to return it.
2. to use someone else's
ideas, ways of doing things,
etc., as your own. **borrowed.**

bunt (bunt) *verb.* to bat a
baseball lightly so that it
does not go beyond the
infield.

busi·ness (biz′nis) *noun.*
1. work that someone does
to earn money. **2.** a place
where work is done or
things are made or sold. **3.**
a matter or affair: The girls
met to make rules and talk
about other club *business.*

bunt

157

C

canopy

customer

can·o·py (kan′ə pē) *noun.*
1. a cloth or other covering set up as a roof above a throne, bed, etc. **2.** something that covers like a canopy: The trees arched above our heads to make a *canopy* or roof over the trail.

cham·ber (chām′bər) *noun.*
1. a room, usually a bedroom. **2.** a large room used for meetings, such as an assembly hall.

charm (chärm) *noun.*
1. something believed to have magical powers, either good or evil. **2.** a small object on a bracelet or necklace. **3.** a physical feature or a personal characteristic that is pleasing, delightful, or attractive.

choice (chois) *noun.* **1.** the act of choosing or picking. **2.** having the chance, power, or right to choose. **3.** someone or something chosen.

chore (chôr) *noun.* **1.** the regular light work such as that done at home or on a farm: His *chores* on the farm included feeding chickens. **2.** a task that is difficult or uninteresting. **chores.**

com·mu·ni·cate (kə myoo′nə kāt) *verb.* to make something known to others; to give or share information: Long ago, some Native Americans could *communicate* by sending smoke signals.

com·plain (kəm plān′) *verb.* to tell about or show pain or unhappiness about something.

con·cen·trate (kon′sən trāt) *verb.* to focus all your attention on something: He will *concentrate* on learning how to play the piano.

con·gress·man (kong′grəs mən) *noun.* an elected official who votes on laws in Congress. **congressmen.**

coun·cil (koun′s'l) *noun.* **1.** a group of people who meet to make plans or decisions. **2.** a group of people elected to make the laws for a town.

cus·to·mer (kus′tə mər) *noun.* a person who buys, often again and again, from the same place. **customers.**

D

---

dap·ple (dap″l) *adjective.* marked with spots; streaked; mottled. —*verb.* to mark or to become marked with spots or patches: The trail through the forest was *dappled* with sunlight. **dappled.**

dawn (dôn) *verb.* **1.** to begin to be day; to grow light. **2.** to begin to happen. —*noun.* the first light of day.

deaf (def) *adjective.* **1.** not able to hear or not able to hear well. **2.** not wanting to hear or listen.

de·ci·sion (di sizh′ən) *noun.* the act of making up your mind about something, or the choice decided on: He made a *decision* about what to wear.

des·ti·na·tion (des′tə nā′shən) *noun.* the place where someone is going.

dis·please (dis plēz′) *verb.* to anger or dissatisfy; to be bothered by: They were *displeased* by the long lines of people outside the movie theater. **displeased.**

a fat	oi oil	ch chin
ā ape	oo look	sh she
ä car, father	ōō tool	th thin
e ten	ou out	*th* then
er care	u up	zh leisure
ē even	ur fur	nĝ ring
i hit		
ir here	ə = a *in* ago	
ī bite, fire	e *in* agent	
o lot	i *in* unity	
ō go	o *in* collect	
ô law, horn	u *in* focus	

E

---

em·bar·rass (im ber′əs) *verb.* to make feel uncomfortable or uneasy. —**embarrassed** *adjective.* self-conscious; ashamed.

emp·ty (emp′tē) *adjective.* having nothing inside. —*verb.* to take everything out of a jar, bottle, etc.

es·pe·cial·ly (ə spesh′əl ē) *adverb.* mostly; in particular: I like vegetables, *especially* carrots.

ex·it (eg′zit *or* ek′sit) *noun.* a way out of a place, such as a door. —*verb.* to go out; to leave.

dawn

exit

159

Farmhand is a compound word made up of *farm* and *hand*. *Hand* in this case refers to a person who works with his or her hands.

F

fame (fām) *noun.* known by many people through books, television, newspapers, etc.

farm·hand (färm′hand) *noun.* a person who works on a farm to earn money: The *farmhand* helped the farmer plow his fields. **farmhands.**

fault (fôlt) *noun.* **1.** a thing or problem that keeps something or someone from being perfect: He has many *faults,* but he is still my friend. **2.** a mistake. **3.** being the cause of something unwanted. **faults.**

fa·vor·ite (fā′vər it) *noun.* a person or thing that is liked better than others. —*adjective.* best liked; preferred: The girl liked to play many sports but baseball was her *favorite.*

fend·er (fen′dər) *noun.* a metal piece over each wheel of a car that protects the car from mud, stones, etc. **fenders.**

flock (flok) *noun.* a group of animals or birds that eat and travel together: The *flock* of birds was so big that it seemed to cover the sky.

flock

G

gar·ment (gär′mənt) *noun.* a piece of clothing, such as a skirt, a pair of pants, etc. **garments.**

goal (gōl) *noun.* **1.** the destination at the end of a race or trip. **2.** a purpose toward which one's actions are aimed: Their *goal* was to finish cleaning the house before the guests arrived. **3.** a net, line, or pocket over or into which a ball must go for a team or player to score in certain games.

H

hes·i·tate (hez′ə tāt) *verb.* **1.** to stop or hold back for a moment as if feeling unsure. **2.** to feel unwilling to do something. **hesitated.**

hike (hīk) *noun.* a long walk, especially through the woods or in the countryside.

hon·or (on′ər) *noun.* **1.** a sign of respect: It was an *honor* to be chosen for the advanced class. **2.** credit or glory, as in winning a prize. **3.** good name. **honour.**

hood (hʊod) *noun.* **1.** a piece that covers the head and neck, often attached to a jacket or coat. **2.** a metal cover in the front of an automobile over the engine.

house·hold (hous′hōld) *noun.* all the people who live in a house, especially a family.

hug (hug) *verb.* **1.** to put the arms around and hold close in a loving way. **2.** to keep close. **hugging.**

I

ig·nore (ig nôr′) *verb.* to act as if something is not happening: Try to *ignore* the noises from the street and just keep talking.

in·ning (in′iñg) *noun.* a part of a baseball game in which both teams get a turn at bat; there are usually nine *innings* in a baseball game: The score was tied so they played extra *innings.*

in·ter·rupt (in tə rupt′) *verb.* **1.** to make a break in something, as in someone talking: He *interrupted* the lesson when he came late to class. **2.** to keep something from going on; to cut off. **interrupted.**

in·tro·duce (in trə dōos′ *or* in trə dyōos′) *verb.* to present or make known to others. **introduces.**

in·vi·ta·tion (in′və ta′shən) *noun.* **1.** the act of inviting a person to go somewhere or to do something. **2.** the spoken or written way of inviting.

a fat	oi oil	ch chin
ā ape	oo look	sh she
ä car, father	ōo tool	th thin
e ten	ou out	th then
er care	u up	zh leisure
ē even	ur fur	ñg ring
i hit		
ir here	ə = a *in* ago	
ī bite, fire	e *in* agent	
o lot	i *in* unity	
ō go	o *in* collect	
ô law, horn	u *in* focus	

J

jag·uar (jag′wär) *noun.* a large, wild cat that looks like a very big leopard. It has a yellowish coat with black spots and lives in forests from the southwestern U.S. to Argentina: The *jaguar* raced across the open plain chasing his prey.

K

ka·pok (kā′pok) *noun.* **1.** a silk-cotton tree of the East Indies, Africa, and tropical America. **2.** the silky fibers around the seeds of a tropical kapok tree. The fibers are used for stuffing mattresses, life jackets, sleeping bags, etc.

hood

jaguar

keyboard

key·board (kē′bôrd) *noun.*
1. the row or rows of black and white keys on a piano or organ. **2.** the lettered and numbered keys on a computer or typewriter.

L

lan·guage (laṅg′gwij) *noun.*
1. the speech or writing people use to understand each other. **2.** any way of communicating thoughts or feelings, such as the way sign language uses hand gestures to mean words. **3.** the written or spoken words of a certain group of people: My pen pal speaks English as well as the Korean *language.*

li·brar·y (lī′brer′ē) *noun.* a place where a collection of books, magazines, records, or films is kept for reading or borrowing.

lit·er·ar·y (lit′ə rer′ē) *adjective.*
1. having to do with the written work of a country, a time in history, etc., that people enjoy reading.
2. having to do with writing.

Marathon races are so named because of a messenger in Greece over two thousand years ago. This messenger ran 26 miles from a city named Marathon to the city of Athens. He delivered the message that the Greeks had defeated the Persians in battle. Modern marathons are the same distance that the ancient messenger ran.

M

mag·a·zine (mag ə zēn′ *or* mag′ə zēn) *noun.* a regular publication with stories, information, pictures, etc., usually coming out once each week or month. **magazines.**

mar·a·thon (mar′ə thon) *noun.* a race run on foot, about 26 miles long.

may·or (mā′ər *or* mer) *noun.* the person elected by the people of the city or town to be in charge of its government.

mem·o·ry (mem′ər ē) *noun.*
1. the act of remembering things. **2.** anything that someone remembers: Her good *memories* of summer camp gave her pleasure all winter long. **3.** the part of a computer that stores information. **memories.**

mes·sen·ger (mes″n jər) *noun.* a person who carries mail or things from one place to another: The *messenger* picked up the package at my house and delivered it to the bank.

mil·let (mil′it) *noun.* **1.** a kind of grass grown for hay. **2.** the seeds of this grass, or grain, as used as food in some parts of the world.

min·now (min′ō) *noun.* a very small fish. **minnows.**

mis·take (mi stāk′) *noun.* something done incorrectly or in error.

mous·tache (mə stash *or* mus′tash) *noun.* the hair a man has let grow out on his upper lip.

move·ment (mo͞ov′mənt) *noun.* the act of moving or changing place.

mur·mur (mur′mər) *verb.* **1.** to make a soft, low, steady sound. **2.** to speak under your breath or complain in a very low voice: The children began to *murmur* to each other when the movie didn't start on time. **murmured.**

N

nib·ble (nib″l) *verb.* **1.** to eat quickly in small bites. **2.** to bite carefully.

note (nōt) *noun.* **1.** a word or sentence written to help you remember something. **2.** a short letter. **3.** a musical tone or the symbol that stands for a musical tone as written on paper. **notes.**

O

of·fi·cial (ə fish′əl) *noun.* **1.** a person who holds office, usually in government. **2.** a person who makes sure that the rules are followed in sports. —*adjective.* coming from someone in authority.

out·field·er (out′fēl′dər) *noun.* a baseball player who stays in center, left, or right field. **outfielders.**

o·val (ō′v'l) *adjective.* having a shape like an egg.

ox·y·gen (ok′si jən) *noun.* a colorless, tasteless, odorless gas that is a chemical element. It makes up about one fifth of the air and combines almost all the other elements: All plants and animals need *oxygen* to live.

a fat	oi oil	ch chin
ā ape	o͞o look	sh she
ä car, father	o͞o tool	th thin
e ten	ou out	*th* then
er care	u up	zh leisure
ē even	ur fur	nĝ ring
i hit		
ir here	ə = a *in* ago	
ī bite, fire	e *in* agent	
o lot	i *in* unity	
ō go	o *in* collect	
ô law, horn	u *in* focus	

millet

piano

P

Piano comes from the Italian word, *pianoforte,* which means "soft" and "strong." The inventor of the piano chose this name because the new instrument could be played both softly and loudly.

practice

pause (pôz) *noun.* to break for a moment when talking; stop for a moment.

per·form·ance (pər fôr′məns) *noun.* the act of doing something before an audience.

per·for·mer (pər fôr′mər) *noun.* a person who acts, plays an instrument, or shows another skill before an audience. **performers.**

pi·an·o (pē an′ō) *noun.* a large musical instrument with wire strings in a case and a keyboard.

pitch·er (pich′ər) *noun.* a baseball player who throws the ball so the batters can try to hit it.

plug (plug) *verb.* **1.** to close up a hole. **2.** to work hard and steadily at something: When we came home, the workers were still *plugging* away at digging the trench. **plugging.**

po·em (pō′əm) *noun.* a written work that uses a pattern of sounds, tempo, and words to show an idea or experience that is deeply felt by the writer.

po·et·ry (pō′ə trē) *noun.* **1.** the art of writing poems. **2.** poems.

pol·li·nate (pol′ə nāt) *verb.* to put pollen on the pistil of a flower; to fertilize by carrying pollen from one flower to another: Bees *pollinate* flowers when they fly from one flower to another.

pop·u·lar (pop′yə lər) *adjective.* **1.** being well liked by many people. **2.** liked by a lot of people.

pop·u·lar·i·ty (pop′yə lar′ə tē) *noun.* the state of being well liked.

po·si·tion (pə zish′ən) *noun.* **1.** the way a person or thing is placed. **2.** the place where a person or thing is, especially how near or far from other things. **3.** a job that someone does.

prac·tice (prak′tis) *verb.* **1.** to make a habit of doing something regularly. **2.** to repeat an action in order to become skilled: The losing team needed to *practice* before the next game.

prep·a·ra·tion (prep′ə rā′shən) *noun.* **1.** getting or being ready for something. **2.** doing things to get ready. **preparations.**

print (print) *verb.* **1.** to press letters or designs onto a surface. **2.** to produce writing to be sold. **3.** to write in letters similar to those in books. **printed.**

pub·lish (pub′lish) *verb.* to get a book, magazine, newspaper, etc., printed and brought to market for sale. **published.**

punt (punt) *noun.* the act of kicking a football after it is dropped from the hands but before it hits the ground.

re·lax (ri laks′) *verb.* **1.** to make something loose. **2.** to rest after working or doing something.

re·lief (ri lēf′) *noun.* freedom from pain, worry, or uncomfortable feelings: We were worried, but it is a *relief* to know you are safe.

re·mind (ri mīnd′) *verb.* to make or help someone remember; to tell something to someone again: He *reminded* me that we had a date. **reminded.**

a fat	oi oil	ch chin
ā ape	oo look	sh she
ä car, father	ōō tool	th thin
e ten	ou out	*th* then
er care	u up	zh leisure
ē even	ur fur	ng ring
i hit		
ir here	ə = a *in* ago	
ī bite, fire	e *in* agent	
o lot	i *in* unity	
ō go	o *in* collect	
ô law, horn	u *in* focus	

R

re·ci·tal (ri sīt″l) *noun.* **1.** the act of telling every part of a story. **2.** a story told like this. **3.** a music or dance program where people perform on stage alone or in a group.

re·cov·er (ri kuv′ər) *verb.* **1.** to get back something that was lost. **2.** to get well again after being sick: I am sure that she will *recover* soon from her bad cold.

re·frig·er·a·tor (ri frij′ə rāt′or) *noun.* a machine or room that keeps food, drinks, etc., cold and fresh.

S

scene (sēn) *noun.* the place and time of a play or story.

sched·ule (skej′ool) *noun.* **1.** a list of times at which things will happen; timetable: I checked my *schedule* so I wouldn't be late. **2.** a list of things to be done with time limits given in which those things must be done.

sep·a·rate (sep′ə rāt) *verb.* **1.** to set apart. **2.** to put something between other things. **3.** to go away from one another. —**separated** *adjective.* set apart; divided.

punt

relax

165

se·ri·ous (sir′ē əs) *adjective.*
1. having thoughts that are deeply felt; important. **2.** not joking or fooling around; sincere: John is *serious* about completing his project on time.

serv·ant (sur′vənt) *noun.* someone who works in another person's home as cook, butler, maid, gardener, etc.

short·stop (sнôrt′stop) *noun.* a baseball player who fields the balls hit between second and third base.

sigh (sī) *noun.* a long, deep breathing sound made when sad, tired, or relieved: The student gave a *sigh* of relief when he learned he had passed the history test.

sign (sīn) *noun.* a word, picture, or action that tells of something else. —*verb.* using a part of the body to show or mean something, as in nodding the head, waving the hand, etc. **signs.**

sign language (sīn lang̃′gwij) *noun.* a system of hand gestures used to talk with people who are deaf.

slave (slāv) *noun.* **1.** a person owned by someone else. **2.** a person who is controlled by something else.

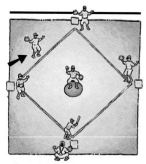
shortstop

sloth

slith·er (slith′ər) *verb.* to move with a sliding or gliding motion: The snake quietly *slithered* down the tree and into the grass. **slithered.**

sloth (slôth *or* slōth) *noun.*
1. a lack of interest in work or any other activity; laziness. **2.** an animal that moves very slowly and lives in trees in South America, often hanging upside down from the branches.

sort (sôrt) *noun.* **1.** a group of things that have something that is the same. **2.** type or kind: There are many *sorts* of toys in the store. **sorts.**

stage (stāj) *noun.* the raised platform in a theater on which actors and entertainers perform.

suf·fer (suf′ər) *verb.* **1.** to feel pain; to be uncomfortable. **2.** to put up with problems, pain, worry, etc.

sug·gest (səg jest′) *verb.* to bring to mind as something to consider or think over.

sus·pi·cious (sə spish′əs) *adjective.* **1.** thinking something is wrong without knowing for sure. **2.** questioning whether or not you can be sure about something.

T

tal·ent (tal′ənt) *noun.* a special ability that a person has from birth.

tem·per (tem′pər) *noun.*
1. the way you feel; mood.
2. anger: She has quite a *temper;* she yelled at everybody.

throat (thrōt) *noun.* **1.** the front of the neck. **2.** the part of the neck through which air, food, and water pass from the mouth to the stomach or lungs.

ti·tled (tīt″ld) *adjective.*
1. having a special title such as lord, knight, lady, etc.
2. having a title or name such as the name of a book.

troupe (troop) *noun.* a group of people who have banded together to do something; a company, especially of actors, singers, etc.: The drama *troupe* traveled from town to town performing plays.

V

val·or (val′ər) *noun.* courage or bravery. **valour.**

W

webbed (webd) *adjective.* having the toes joined by pieces of skin or flesh: Ducks have *webbed* feet.

wig·gle (wig″l) *verb.* to twist or turn quickly from side to side. **wiggled.**

with·er (with′ər) *verb.* **1.** to lose freshness; to dry up; shrivel: The plants *withered* because we forgot to water them. **2.** to lose strength. **3.** to make fearful or ashamed.

wor·thy (wur′thē) *adjective.*
1. having value or being wanted. **2.** being good enough for something.

writ·er (rīt′ər) *noun.* someone who writes books, essays, poems, etc., especially as a way to earn a living; author.

a fat	oi oil	ch chin
ā ape	oo look	sh she
ä car, father	ōō tool	th thin
e ten	ou out	*th* then
er care	u up	zh leisure
ē even	ur fur	ng ring
i hit		
ir here	ə = a *in* ago	
ī bite, fire	e *in* agent	
o lot	i *in* unity	
ō go	o *in* collect	
ô law, horn	u *in* focus	

throat

167

ABOUT THE
Authors & *Illustrators*

GWENDOLYN BROOKS

The poet Gwendolyn Brooks was born in Topeka, Kansas. She says, "I loved poetry very early and began to put rhymes together at about seven." At the age of thirteen, her poem "Eventide" was accepted and printed in a children's magazine. When she was sixteen, she began submitting poems to a newspaper, and more than 75 of them were published. Ms. Brooks won the Pulitzer Prize in poetry in 1950 for *Annie Allen. (Born 1917)*

ANN CAMERON

From the time Ann Cameron was in the third grade, she wanted to be a writer. She says, "A book is something like a message in a bottle that an author throws out to sea; you never know whom it might reach, or how much it might mean to them." Ann Cameron has this advice for young writers: "Your story, if it's really the way you want to tell it, can never be wrong the way an arithmetic answer is wrong; and even if your mother, your father, your teacher, or your best friend doesn't understand it, it's still right for you." *(Born 1943)*

LYNNE CHERRY

▲ Lynne Cherry spends a lot of time in the woods observing nature, which has helped her learn how to illustrate plants and animals well. She says, "Art is a wonderful way to express the beauty I see in life." Ms. Cherry also wants to help make the world a better place through her books. She wrote *The Great Kapok Tree* to warn children that man is rapidly destroying the rain forests of the world. *(Born 1952)*

RAY CRUZ

✳ Ray Cruz was born in New York City and still lives there. He studied at the High School of Art and Design, at Pratt Institute, and at Cooper Union. He has been an illustrator for over twenty years. During his career, he has illustrated about a dozen children's books and magazines. When he isn't working his chief interest is the protection of our environment and wildlife. *(Born 1933)*

CHIEF DAN GEORGE

■ Chief Dan George, a member of the Coast-Salish tribe, was born in Vancouver, British Columbia. As a child he learned the crafts and traditional ways of his people. Later, he worked as a longshoreman and served as Chief of his Reserve for twelve years. When he was 60 years old, Chief Dan George decided to become an actor. Some of his movies were *Little Big Man, The Outlaw Josey Wales,* and *Harry and Tonto.* He also wrote two books of prose-poetry, *My Heart Soars* and *My Spirit Soars. (1899–1981)*

LEE BENNETT HOPKINS

▲ Lee Bennett Hopkins writes about his interviews with writers and illustrators. He also writes poems for young people and puts together anthologies, or collections, of other people's poems. He reads thousands of poems and chooses the twenty that he thinks children will enjoy most. He says, "I love doing children's books. Each one is a new challenge, a new day, a new spring for me." *(Born 1938)*

JOHANNA HURWITZ

✳ Johanna Hurwitz writes books for young people. She is also a children's librarian. She says, "My parents met in a bookstore and there has never been a moment when books were not important in my life. I loved the library so much that I made the firm decision by age ten that someday I would become a librarian. And I also planned that I would write books too." Johanna Hurwitz likes to write many letters to friends and relatives. She thinks the letter writing she does is good training for her book writing. *(Born 1937)*

ISSA

■ Issa is the pen name for the Japanese poet, Kobayashi Issa. In his haiku, Issa uses ordinary words to describe everyday subjects, such as the wind blowing so softly that it doesn't scare the butterflies. This simple, sentimental haiku has endeared him to the Japanese people. *(1763–1827)*

LI PO

▲ Many people think Li Po is China's greatest poet.
He lived a long time ago, during the Tang dynasty in
the eighth century. Li Po liked to pretend he was a
member of China's royal family but he wasn't. He just
had the same family name. He often found himself in
exile for political reasons and his nickname was the
"banished Immortal." His poetry reveals his lively
imagination and romantic personality.

ADA B. LITCHFIELD

✳ Ada B. Litchfield grew up on Cape Cod, in
Massachusetts. She began writing when she was a
little girl. She has been a teacher and editor. Besides
writing books for children, she has written many
scripts for educational television. *(Born 1916)*

ALONZO LOPEZ

■ Alonzo Lopez, a Papago Native American, was born
in Pima County, Arizona. He learned to write poetry in
high school at the Institute of American Indian Arts in
Santa Fe, New Mexico. Several of his poems have been
published in *The Whispering Wind,* a wonderful book
of poems written by Native American students at the
Institute. He graduated from Wesleyan University in
1973 with a degree in Anthropology.

A. A. MILNE

※ Alan Alexander Milne began writing when he was seventeen. He said, "It was in the Christmas holidays of 1899 that I discovered the itch for writing which has never quite left me." He started out by writing poems. Later he began writing stories. Some of his stories are about a boy named Christopher Robin and a bear named Winnie-the-Pooh. Milne's only son was also named Christopher Robin. *(1882–1956)*

ERNEST H. SHEPARD

■ Ernest Howard Shepard was born in England where he lived all his life. He said that he had always intended to be an artist of some kind. He drew cartoons for the famous English magazine *Punch* for nearly fifty years. Mr. Shepard also illustrated many children's books, including *The Wind in the Willows, The Reluctant Dragon,* and *The Secret Garden.* He is probably best known for illustrating the Christopher Robin books by A. A. Milne. He had two children, a son and a daughter. His daughter illustrated the Mary Poppins books. In 1972, Ernest H. Shepard was the recipient of the Order of the British Empire in recognition of his artistic works. *(1879–1976)*

JOHN STEPTOE

▲ John Steptoe was a painter and a writer and also taught at the Brooklyn Music School. He illustrated all of his own books as well as books for other writers. He received the Lewis Carroll Shelf Award for the book *Stevie*. He said that one of the reasons he began writing books for young people was the need for "books that black children could honestly relate to." John Steptoe's book, *Mufaro's Beautiful Daughters,* was named a Caldecott Honor book and won the 1987 Boston Globe Horn Book Award. *(1950–1989)*

ANN STRUGNELL

✳ Ann Strugnell was born in Coventry, England, where she attended the College of Art and Design. She studied sculpture before she decided to become a book illustrator. Her drawings are a delightful combination of realism and humor. Among the books Ms. Strugnell has illustrated are *Into the Painted Bear Lair* and *The Fool and the Dancing Bear.*

JUDITH VIORST

■ Judith Viorst began writing poetry when she was seven years old. She says she wrote "terrible poems about dead dogs, mostly." She did not become a successful writer until she was grown. Now she is an award-winning author. Judith Viorst says, "Most of my children's books are for or about my own children. . . ." *(Born 1931)*

AUTHOR INDEX

Grateful acknowledgment is made to the following publishers, authors, and agents for their permission to reprint copyrighted material. Every effort has been made to locate all copyright proprietors; any errors or omissions in copyright notice are inadvertent and will be corrected in future printings as they are discovered.

Alexander and the Terrible, Horrible, No Good, Very Bad Day by Judith Viorst and illustrated by Ray Cruz. Reprinted by permission of the American publisher, Atheneum Publishers, an imprint of Macmillan Publishing Company, of the British publisher, Angus & Robertson (UK), and of the author's agents, Lescher & Lescher, Ltd. Text copyright © 1972 by Judith Viorst. Illustrations copyright © 1972 by Ray Cruz.

"And My Heart Soars" by Chief Dan George. © 1974 by Chief Dan George and Helmut Hirnschall. Reprinted by permission of Hancock House Publishers Ltd.

"The Boy Who Cried Wolf" by Genie Iverson, © 1989 by Genie Iverson. Reprinted by permission of the author.

"A Day When Frogs Wear Shoes" from *More Stories Julian Tells* by Ann Cameron, illustrated by Ann Strugnell. Text copyright © 1986 by Ann Cameron. Illustrations copyright © 1986 by Ann Strugnell. Reprinted by permission of the American publisher, Alfred A. Knopf, Inc., a Division of Random House, Inc., and of the British publisher, Victor Gollancz Ltd.

"Eagle Flight" by Alonzo Lopez, from *The Whispering Wind* by Terry Allen. Copyright © 1972 by the Institute of American Indian Arts. Reprinted by permission of Doubleday, a division of Bantam Doubleday Dell Publishing Group, Inc.

"The Firefly" by Li T'ai Po, reprinted from *A Garden of Peonies*, translated by Henry H. Hart with the permission of the publishers, Stanford University Press. Copyright 1938 by the Board of Trustees of the Leland Stanford Junior University. Copyright renewed 1966 by Henry S. Hart.

"A giant firefly" from *An Introduction to Haiku* by Harold G. Henderson. Copyright © 1958 by Harold G. Henderson. Reprinted by permission of Doubleday, a division of Bantam Doubleday Dell Publishing Group, Inc.

The Great Kapok Tree, written and illustrated by Lynne Cherry, copyright © 1990 by Lynne Cherry, reprinted by permission of Harcourt Brace Jovanovich, Inc.

"In Which Piglet Meets a Heffalump" from *Winnie-the-Pooh* by A. A. Milne, illustrated by Ernest H. Shepard. Copyright 1926 by E.P. Dutton, renewed 1954 by A.A. Milne. Text and art used by permission of the American publishers, Dutton Children's Books, a division of Penguin Books USA Inc., text by permission of the British publishers, Methuen Children's Books, a division of Octopus Publishing Group Library, and art by permission of the British agents, Curtis Brown Group Ltd., London. Copyright under the Berne Convention.

"Jason Wants a Library" by Margaret Tuley Patton, © 1989 by Silver, Burdett & Ginn Inc.

"Lee Bennett Hopkins Interviews Johanna Hurwitz," © 1989 by Silver, Burdett & Ginn Inc.

Mufaro's Beautiful Daughters, written and illustrated by John Steptoe. Copyright © 1987 John Steptoe. All rights reserved. Reprinted with permission of William Morrow & Company, Inc./Publishers, New York, and of Murphy and Zissu, Attorneys-at-Law, for the author's estate.

"Narcissa" from *Bronzeville Boys and Girls* by Gwendolyn Brooks. Copyright © 1956, renewed 1984 by Gwendolyn Brooks Blakely. Reprinted by permission of Harper*Collins* Publishers.

"Phillis Wheatley, America's First Black Poet" by Kacey Brown, © 1989 by Silver, Burdett & Ginn Inc.

"The Recital" by Johanna Hurwitz, © 1989 by Silver, Burdett & Ginn Inc.

"Sports Signals" by Gary Apple, © 1989 by Silver, Burdett & Ginn Inc.

Words in Our Hands by Ada B. Litchfield. Text Copyright © 1980 by Ada B. Litchfield. Reprinted by permission of Albert Whitman & Company.

COVER: Gregory Alexander R.W.S.

ILLUSTRATIONS: 4-7, Tamar Haber-Schaim; 12-20, Rae Eklund; 21, Kathy Parkenson; 38-50, Ann Strugnell; 51, Danielle Clifford; 60-61, Troy Howell; 62-69, Ray Cruz; 74-84, Lynne Cherry; 86-87, Vivienne Flesher; 88-100, Cathy Diefendorf; 101, Sara Deponte; 102-108, Lane Gregory; 110-122, John Steptoe; 123, Margery Mintz; 124-125, David Taylor; 126-136, Ashley Wolff; 137, Karen Watkins; 138-155, Ernest H. Shepard; 157-159, Barbara Lanza; 160, Roberta Holmes; 161, Barbara Lanza; 163, Deirdre Griffin; 164, Claudia Sargent; 165, Diane Dawson Hearn; 166, Claudia Sargent, Barbara Lanza;167, Diane Dawson Hearn; 168-173 , Tamar Haber-Schaim.

PHOTOGRAPHY: 8-9, Bob Firth; 9, BOY JUGGLING SHELLS, ink and color on paper by Katsushika Hokusai, Japanese, (1760-1849), 14.76.59.4, © The Metropolitan Museum of Art, New York, Charles Stewart Smith Collection, Gift of Mrs. Charles Stewart Smith, Jr., and Howard Caswell Smith, in Memory of Charles Stewart Smith, 1914. Photograph by Malcolm Varon; 11, supplied by SBG/Morristown; 22, 25, Eduardo Patino; 27, The Bettmann Archive; 29-36, Laird Roberts; 37, Michael & Patricia Fogden; 52, The Granger Collection; 54, Thomas Bewick, Dover Books; 57, *George Washington* by Rembrandt Peale, National Portrait Gallery, Smithsonian Institution; 59, John Trumbull, *The Declaration of Independence, 4 July 1776,* © Yale University Art Gallery; 70-71, David Young-Wolff/ PhotoEdit; 71, THE LETTER, ca. 1891, Mary Stevenson Cassatt, American, 1844-1926. Color print with dry point, soft-ground and aquatint. 13⅜ x 8⁵⁄₁₆ in. Gift of William Emerson and Charles Henry Hayden Fund. Courtesy, Museum of Fine Arts, Boston; 73, Ken O'Donoghue;102-103, Ken Levine/Allsport; 106, Steven Goldstein, courtesy, St. Louis Cardinals; 107, Focus on Sports; 123, (l) James Ropiequet Schmidt, courtesy, John Steptoe Estate, (r) John Steptoe, courtesy, John Steptoe Estate; 159, Stephen G. Maka; 161, Carla Palau; 162, 164, © Frank Siteman 1988; 165, Mike Mazzaschi/Stock, Boston; 168, (t) Los Angeles Times, (b) Fernando Diaz Rivera; 169, (t) courtesy, Harcourt Brace Jovanovich, (b) UPI/Bettmann Newsphotos; 170, (t) Antique Images/Putnam, (m) Viking Penguin; 171, (t) Historical Pictures Service, provided by the author; 172, (t, b) The Bettmann Archive; 173, (t) James Ropiequet Schmidt, courtesy John Steptoe Estate. 173 (b) Milton Viorst.